THE
LIGHT
DOCTOR

USING LIGHT TO
BOOST HEALTH,
IMPROVE SLEEP,
AND LIVE LONGER

MARTIN MOORE-EDE, M.D., Ph.D.

Former professor, Harvard Medical School
Director, Circadian Light Research Center

THE LIGHT DOCTOR

Using Light to Boost Health, Improve Sleep, and Live Longer

by

Martin Moore-Ede M.D., Ph.D.

First Edition 2024

Published by CIRCADIAN® Books

2 Main Street, Suite 340, Stoneham, MA 02180, USA

Designed by

Kerry Ellis

Library of Congress Control Number 2024937756
ISBN 979-8-9906869-08

Portions of this book were first published as an online serial
on Substack at lightdoctormartinmooreede.substack.com

Dedication

With appreciation for my colleagues, including more than 30,000 scientists from all over the globe, who have published more than 24,000 peer-reviewed scientific articles on the interactions between light and circadian clocks, and who have helped us understand why the right light at the right time is so important for health and well-being.

Preface

The light we see is as important for our health as the food we eat, the water we drink, and the air we breathe. For most of human existence, our ancestors lived with the natural 24-hour light-dark cycle, spending each day in natural daylight and sleeping in the dark at night. But since the widespread introduction of electric light, more than 90% of our time is spent indoors, under unhealthful and human-unfriendly electric light, which disrupts our circadian clocks and greatly increases the risk of cancer, obesity, diabetes, heart disease, and hundreds of other diseases.

Today's LED fixtures, light bulbs, and screens are designed to produce cheap light with little regard for human health. Like DDT and asbestos, they are dangerously flawed technologies. THE LIGHT DOCTOR reveals extensive scientific evidence establishing the risks of blue-rich artificial light at night. Furthermore, it provides the practical information you need to counteract these risks at home, and in workplaces, schools, hospitals, and senior care facilities.

Here is how to find and install healthy light bulbs and fixtures for both residential and commercial spaces; how to obtain the lights you need for evening and night use versus daytime, and how to obtain energy-efficient light that is also safe and healthy. You will also learn which outdoor lights to install to avoid harmful effects on wildlife, another inadvertent consequence of the LED revolution.

About the Author

For over 40 years, Dr. Moore-Ede has been a leading world expert on circadian clocks and the health problems caused by electric light at night. As a professor at Harvard Medical School (1975 – 1998), he led the team that located the suprachiasmatic nucleus, the biological clock in the human brain that controls the timing of sleep and wake, and showed how circadian clocks regulate the timing of body functions. His book, *The Clocks That Time Us: Physiology of the Circadian Timing System*, became the leading textbook in hundreds of college courses.

In 1983, Dr Moore-Ede founded the global consulting and technology firm CIRCADIAN® (https://www.circadian.com/) with offices in Boston, London, Amsterdam, Osaka, and Brisbane, which applies circadian physiology to improve the productivity, health, and safety of 24/7 workforces, including over half of the Fortune 500. His international best-selling book, *The Twenty-Four Hour Society: Understanding Human Limits in a World That Never Stops*, was based on this experience.

To address his clients' growing concerns about the harmful

effects of conventional fluorescent and LED lighting on work-force health, safety, and performance, Dr Moore-Ede founded the Circadian Light Research Center in 2010 and spun off the tech start-up CIRCADIAN ZircLight in 2011. He led the team that identified the critical sky-blue signal that synchronizes circadian clocks. This enabled the development of patented LED lights, which provide circadian-optimized light across day and night based on comprehensive medical research.

Dr. Moore-Ede graduated with a First-Class Honors degree in Physiology from the University of London. He received his medical degrees from Guy's Hospital Medical School, and his Ph.D. in Physiology from Harvard University.

Contents

Introduction

Questions to Ask Before
Switching on the Lights

L auren thought she had seen everything and could handle any crisis that came in through the emergency room doors. At the age of 36, she was at the peak of her career as an ER physician at a major teaching hospital.

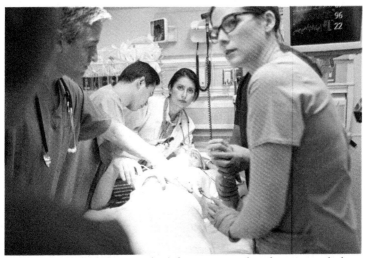

Exposure to bright lights on night shifts causes circadian disruption, which is linked to many illnesses, including breast cancer
(istock.com/monkeybusinessimages)

She didn't think much about the bright fluorescent lights illuminating the ER. To her, they were critical for examining and treating the gunshot wounds, motor vehicle accident injuries, and the full panoply of human disease and distress that came into the ER. They were especially helpful since she had chosen for the past ten years to work 12-hour night shifts when the ER is at its busiest. That way, she could spend quality time at home with her young children during their awake hours.

She certainly didn't dream of the damage the hospital lights were doing to her. That is until she found the lump in her right breast. She was terrified when the pathology came back showing invasive ductal carcinoma invading her surrounding breast tissue and armpit nodes. No one had told her of the risks of light at night, and here she was, going through chemotherapy and surgery and facing the shock of a derailed life. What Lauren didn't know, despite her extensive medical training, was that the light we see is as critical to our health as the air we breathe, the food we eat, and the water we drink.

Just as junk food can taste good, unhealthy electric light can look good. Our senses can be deceived and not protect our well-being or our health. Lauren had never wondered:

- Why do women who have never seen electric light rarely get breast cancer? Why is it an uncommon disease in women who have been blind since birth or live where electricity has not yet reached?

- Why have breast cancer rates surged more than five-fold in the past 100 years, depending on the amount of electric light you use? Why did it become the most common cancer in women only after Thomas Edison gave us the ability to conquer the night?

- Why do young nurses and doctors like her who work the night shift suffer 50% more breast cancer than those who work daytime hours? That's 50% higher than the already elevated rates in the electrified world.

We will discuss this evidence in detail in Chapter 1: *Edison's Cancer Epidemic*.

For most of human existence, our ancestors were bathed each day in natural daylight and slept in the dark at night. But since the widespread introduction of electric light, more than 90% of our time is spent indoors. We have substituted the natural 24-hour light-dark cycle with human-unfriendly electric light. We have failed to recognize the dark side of our current electric lights at night.

The Risk of Metabolic Diseases

John was one of those many people who preferred to have the lights on during sleep because it comforted him. Ever since he was a kid, he had been afraid of the dark and the shadows that lurked in the corners of the bedroom. Then later on, after his wife died, he found leaving the TV on distracted him from the sadness and anxious thoughts that flooded his mind. He was gaining weight and had been diagnosed with high blood pressure and diabetes. And now he had elevated PSA levels, which suggested he might have prostate cancer, so there was a lot to worry about in the wee hours of the morning. Besides having the lights on made it less likely for him to trip over something on those middle-of-the-night trips to the bathroom, which got more frequent as he got older.

But no one had ever told John that those bedroom lights caused his medical bad luck. None of his doctors or counselors had ever wondered:

Over 50% of elderly people sleep with the lights on, which approximately doubles the risk of obesity, diabetes, and hypertension. (iStock.com/ajr_images)

- Why do elderly people who sleep with the lights on at night have almost twice the rate of obesity, diabetes, and heart disease? Why do they suffer early disability and death just because they failed to switch off the lights?

- Why do lights at night switch on the hunger centers in the brain? What causes the constant snacking that leads to obesity?

- Why do men who sleep in well-illuminated bedrooms have more than twice the rate of prostate cancer? Why do they lose the protection of the cancer-suppressing hormone melatonin?

It is time we recognize that "inhaling" unhealthy electric light after sunset is the "tobacco" equivalent of breast cancer in women. And, prostate cancer in men   And, diabetes, obesity and heart disease, and much more.

THE LIGHT DOCTOR | 5

We will discuss this evidence in detail in Chapter 2: *Goodbye Milky Way*

The Disruption of Sleep

We should also wonder:

- Why do 25% of us suffer from insomnia, and 35% of us are chronically sleep-deprived? How does switching on the wrong electric lights in the evening delay and disrupt our sleep?

- Why are our children so exhausted the next day after playing games on their blue-rich LED screens before bed? How do the blue wavelengths alert their brains before bedtime, disrupt their sleep, and shift their circadian clocks?

It is all because we have failed to use the right light at the right time of day.

We will discuss this evidence in detail in Chapter 3: *Clockwork Blue*

My Own Awakening

"Wake-Up Moore-Ede!" the Surgeon-in-Chief yelled, as I let the retractor slip during emergency surgery. It was 3 am in the morning and my head had bobbed, and my hand slipped, in the middle of a challenging operation. I was a motivated and ambitious young surgeon, and being yelled at in the operating room by the Surgeon-in-Chief was not good for my career ... or for the patient.

It was because my circadian sleep-wake cycle had been scrambled after working a year of 36-hour shifts under bright hospital lights.

This was the start of a lifetime journey – and a personal

mission – to understand circadian clocks, how they interact with light, and how that determines our health. I left my career as a surgeon to enter the Ph.D. program at Harvard Medical School to study the physiology of circadian rhythms. Then, as a professor on the Harvard Medical School faculty – a position I held for 23 years – I built a Laboratory for Circadian Physiology and recruited a brilliant team of graduate students and postdocs. With my scientific colleagues, we located the circadian clock in the human brain, discovered how it is synchronized by light, and revealed the role electric light at night plays in disrupting circadian rhythms and negatively affecting our health.

Once it became clear by 2010 that electric lights were causing cancer and many other serious diseases, I founded the Circadian Light Research Center to investigate the problem. I then raised funds to start a company, CIRCADIAN® ZircLight, in 2011 to develop a solution. We identified a narrow band of blue wavelengths in light responsible for synchronizing our circadian rhythms during the day but harming our health at night. Then we solved this unhealthy lighting problem by spectrally engineering and manufacturing healthy circadian lights, which deliver circadian blue-rich light during the day and circadian blue-depleted light at night.

We have now proven the benefits of healthy circadian lights. We have provided attractive white light, which restored the cancer-protecting melatonin hormone at night, prevented the clock shifts and sleep disruptions caused by light at night, and reversed the diabetic state caused by regular blue-pump LED lights in healthy people. Then, to scale up the production and availability of these healthy circadian lights, we licensed the rights to several major lighting companies, and sold the lighting intellectual property rights to Korrus, a company specializing in the multiple dimensions of human-light interaction.

But most people still don't know about the healthy lights and display screens that are now available. And they don't know which blue-blocking glasses are effective and which are merely a placebo.

I have written this book to alert everyone who buys electric lights and blue-emitting display screens. You must protect yourself from the most ubiquitous and convenient of all technologies. You need to know why most LED and fluorescent lights on the market today are devastatingly harmful to your health and must be replaced with healthy circadian lights.

Ultimately, you, the reader, needs to learn about the risks and how to take care of your family and your workplace colleagues. You must know which lights and display screens to ask for and why. You need to advocate for healthy lighting in your schools, hospitals and the senior living facilities caring for your elderly parents. This book is written to help you address this challenge.

What You Will Learn

The first section of THE LIGHT DOCTOR shares more than 20 years of evidence for the harmful effects of insufficient blue-rich light during the day, and too much blue light in the evening and at night. I will show that the impact of electric light on breast cancer is the equivalent of the effect of smoking on lung cancer. Without electric light breast cancer incidence is low, but it is increased multiplefold depending on the amount of blue light exposure during nocturnal hours. The story is similar with obesity, diabetes, heart disease, and hundreds of other medical conditions.

The second section covers the breakthroughs in circadian

lighting solutions and how they were achieved. It reviews the evidence-based science that documents and demonstrates the benefits. This will arm you with the knowledge to distinguish between real versus false claims about circadian lighting.

The third section puts you in the driver's seat. It teaches what to ask for when ordering light fixtures, bulbs, and display screens, and when and how to use circadian lighting. The secret to protecting yourself and your loved ones is using the right light at the right time across all the hours of the daily journey, from when you get up until you return to bed.

Now we know about the dark side of electric light we have the chance to reverse the unintended havoc that ill-designed electric light has wreaked. There are $2.5 Trillion of unhealthy lights in the world that need to be replaced.[1] It all starts with you replacing the lights in your home, your workplace, and wherever else you spend your indoor hours.

After you read this book, you will:

1. Understand the dangers of the lights you currently use.

2. Know how to select lighting for your home that protects and boosts your health.

3. Be equipped to advocate for healthy circadian lighting in your workplace, schools, hospitals, and senior living facilities.

PART 1:

ELECTRIC HAVOC

1

Edison's Cancer Epidemic

There are strong links between the misuse of electric light, circadian rhythm disruption and certain types of cancer, including breast and prostate cancer.

There is nothing more devastating to a family than when a young mother in her 30s or 40s dies of breast cancer. Young children lose their mother's love and guidance through their teenage years. Her career is cut short, and her husband is left to cope alone at the most demanding time of his career. So, it was with my wife's best friend, Teresa. I still remember Teresa and her wedge pattern shoe soles that imprinted distinctive track marks on our carpet, so I always knew when she had visited. She died of breast cancer in her 40s, just after she had completed her graduate training in counseling, leaving behind three sons and a devastated husband.

We know the major causes of many preventable cancers. Smoking causes most lung cancers, asbestos most mesotheliomas, human papillomavirus most cervical cancers. However,

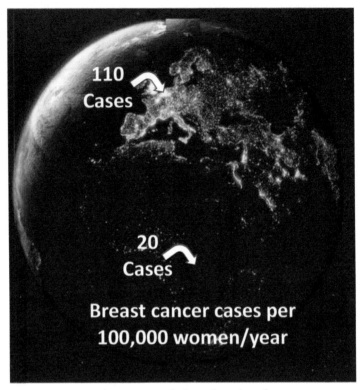

110
Cases

20
Cases

Breast cancer cases per
100,000 women/year

Breast cancer incidence rates are highest where electrification is greatest.
(Adapted from istock.com/ABIDAL)

the enormous growth in breast cancer incidence over the past century was a mystery until the discovery of the impact of electric light.

Thomas Edison's invention of electric light brought us many benefits - and the illusion that we now control the night. But living indoors under inadequate light during the day and using the wrong electric light during the hours of darkness, especially today's energy-efficient blue-rich fluorescent and LED lights, disrupts our circadian clocks and triggers or exacerbates a wide range of illnesses, including breast and prostate cancer.

Based on all the evidence we have today, it looks like blue-rich electric light at night may be the "tobacco" of breast cancer. Women who have never seen electric light rarely get breast cancer. In contrast, women who are regularly exposed to bright electric light after sunset have breast cancer diagnosis rates that are five or more times higher than women with no exposure to electric light.

Just like the lung cancer epidemic caused by smoking, where only 20% of cases occur in non-smokers, breast cancer cases are uncommon in the absence of electric light. There is a base incidence rate of about 20 new cases of breast cancer per 100,000 women per year in populations with little or no access to electric light.[2] This jumps to 90-110 new breast cancer cases each year per 100,000 women in fully electrified Western European and North American populations, and even higher incidence rates in women who are regularly exposed to electric light on night shifts.[3]

Over the years of adulthood, the yearly incidence rate of new diagnoses stacks up so that eventually, 13% of American women will develop breast cancer during their lifetime.[4] This lifetime risk has been progressively creeping upwards since the introduction of blue-rich electric lights that are efficient at producing light that appears bright to the human eye.

Who are those women who had little or no exposure to electric light at night? To find them, we can look back at women before the introduction of electric light. We can also look at the 300 million women today who live in underdeveloped regions, such as rural sub-Saharan Africa, which have never had electricity. And we can look at the 5 million women in the world who are totally blind, and especially those who have been blind since before puberty. All these populations have very low rates of breast cancer.

A well-documented example is Iceland.[5] Remotely located

in the Atlantic Ocean, Iceland was slower than Europe and North America to introduce electricity to its population because fossil fuels had to be imported. The first public power plant was not built until the 1920s when the breast cancer diagnosis rate was 30 per 100,000 women/year, and electric lights did not reach the most homes until the 1950s. As it did, the breast cancer incidence doubled from 30 to 60. By 2000, Iceland became one of the world's largest per capita electricity consumers (which, thanks to geothermal springs is 99% renewable) and had a breast cancer incidence rate approaching that of fully electrified Western Europe.

Countries in the middle of Africa below the Sahara still have little access to electric light, However, that is beginning to change rapidly, and the breast cancer diagnosis rate with it. By 2000, only about 20% of the population of Botswana had access to electricity, and the breast cancer incidence rate was near the base rate of 20 cases per 100,000 women per year.[6] By 2020, electricity had reached 70% of the Botswana population, and we can expect the rate of new breast cancer cases to climb sharply, given it takes five or more years of electric light exposure to take effect.

Even the totally blind may have some light perception; most blindness doesn't occur until old age. However, investigations of women who became totally blind before the age of 65 show they have half the rate of breast cancer diagnosis.[7] The rate is probably much less in the much smaller population of women who became blind before puberty and never saw electric light in their pre-menopausal reproductive years.

Some women in our 24/7 society are exposed to more light at night than average, and their breast cancer incident rates are significantly higher. Millions of women in critical jobs such as nursing and manufacturing regularly work the overnight shift in brightly lit workplaces.

Take, for example, Helen, who started working 14–hour night shifts as an operating room nurse at age 25, specializing in vascular high-tech procedures that were performed under bright fluorescent lights. She had her son at age 24, and her work schedule enabled her to spend time with her child and look after her horses during the day. She first noticed the lump in her breast at age 45, and after it was determined to be malignant, she was given chemotherapy. Subsequently, the ordeal has continued with surgery and 12 radiation treatments.

Individual anecdotes of women, like Helen, who developed breast cancer after exposure to light at night, do not, of course, prove the link. That requires epidemiological research --- the study of the health of large populations of people who are either exposed or not exposed to a potential risk. In this case, it requires controlled studies comparing large numbers of female night shift workers versus large numbers of women who have never worked at night, which balance out other risk factors such as age, smoking history, and number of pregnancies between the two populations.

In 2001, the first large-scale epidemiological studies were published, which indicated that the effects of light at night on breast cancer were real and not just anecdotal:

- Dr. Johnni Hansen at the Danish Cancer Society's Institute of Cancer Epidemiology, reported a 70% increased risk of breast cancer in a study of 7,035 pre-menopausal Danish women aged 30- 54 in the beverage manufacturing, catering and transportation industries, if they had worked predominantly at night for at least six years since 1964.[8]

- Dr. Scott Davis at the University of Washington, and Dr. Richard Stevens, from the University of Connecticut, reported a 60% increased risk of breast cancer in women who worked overnight shifts during the period 1985 to 1995, with the risk increasing with more years of night shift work and more night shifts per week.[9]

- Dr Eva Schernhammer and her team at Harvard Medical School took advantage of the Nurses' Health Study with its long-term tracking of 78,562 female nurses. In a 10-year (1988-1998) prospective follow-up of these nurses, who were 30-55 years old at the start of the study, they found a 36% increase in breast cancer risk among those women who had worked 30 or more years on the night shift.[10]

These studies were all conducted prior to 2000, long before the arrival of LED lights in 2013, so the only lights they were exposed to at night were incandescent, halogen, or fluorescent. As discussed in Chapter 3: *Clockwork Blue*, while incandescent and halogen lights have relatively low blue content, the fluorescent lights in nocturnal workplaces had almost as much circadian-disruptive blue content as today's LEDs.

I may be a little unfair to Thomas Edison by calling this chapter *"Edison's Cancer Epidemic"*. Breast cancer incidence rates remained relatively flat in the USA until 1970, while electric lights were mostly incandescent bulbs with low blue content. But then breast cancer diagnosis rates shot up more than four-fold over the next 40 years from 1970 to 2014, as blue-rich fluorescent lights were widely introduced, and America converted to a twenty-four-hour society where more than 20% of the population worked night shifts under these blue-rich fluorescent lights.[11]

Even among those who don't work the night shift, some women are exposed to more light than others. Women who sleep with the bedroom lights on have higher breast cancer rates than those who sleep in the dark.[9] And women in urbanized areas with full access to electric light and bright streetlights illuminating their windows at night have higher rates of breast cancer than their rural impoverished neighbors with less exposure or access to electric light.[12]

But how does this happen? How exactly does electric light cause breast cancer?

The Light - Melatonin - Cancer Pathway

In 1987, Richard ("Bugs") Stevens, an epidemiologist at the US Department of Energy's Pacific Northwest National Labs, was the first person to suggest a link between the use of electric light at night and breast cancer.[13] At that time, there were many ideas on what might account for the rapid growth in breast cancer incidence and the disparities between the developed and underdeveloped countries of the world. But the leading contenders, such as racial differences, the age that women had children, and dietary fat content, were each ruled out one by one by the scientific evidence.

When "Bugs" Stevens postulated the increasing use of electric light was inducing the rise in breast cancer, he suggested a clear causal pathway. First, light at night is known to suppress the production of the pineal hormone, melatonin, and second, melatonin has powerful effects in suppressing the growth of cancer tumors. He suggested that reduced melatonin production when electric lights are switched on after sunset allowed tumors, that otherwise would have been suppressed, to grow unchecked.

It was a novel and "way-out" idea at the time. But in the

last 35 years, a voluminous body of research has verified and expanded upon this causal pathway in both human and animal studies.

Some classic studies were conducted by Professor David Blask and his colleagues at Tulane University in New Orleans, using rats implanted with human breast cancer grafts.[14] The human breast cancer tumors grew rapidly when the lights were left on at night in the rats' cages so that their melatonin production was suppressed. They grew much more slowly when the rats had the lights switched off at night, and normal melatonin production could occur.

That melatonin was a key factor responsible for this effect of light was shown in an ingenious study designed by Dr Blask. Blood was collected from young women either sitting in the dark at night at Thomas Jefferson University in Philadelphia, when their melatonin levels were high, or after sitting under bright lights at night when their melatonin levels were low. The blood samples from these two groups of women were then shipped by FedEx overnight to Tulane University and infused into the rats. The melatonin-rich blood samples, from women who were kept in the dark, significantly slowed the rate of breast tumor growth, whereas the low melatonin blood samples from women who were under the lights, allowed rapid breast tumor growth in the rats. As Professor Blask stated, "These mechanistic studies are the first to provide a rational biological explanation for the increased breast cancer risk in female night shift workers."

However, the cancer risk from light exposure at night is not simply a matter of melatonin suppression. Our bodies are precisely timed machines with circadian clocks in virtually every cell of the body, all coordinated by a master pacemaker called the suprachiasmatic nucleus (or SCN for short).[15] It is located in the primitive part of the brain where most of our automated "no thought needed" systems are found. As long as we lived in the natural 24-hour world order of regular dawns and dusks with bright sunlight followed by dim moonlight or starlight, all these millions of clocks operated in harmonic synchrony.

But our ready access to electric lights has disrupted this well-ordered natural world. Nowadays electric light enables us to spend most of our daytime indoors under lights much dimmer than natural daylight and extends our waking hours in the evening under lights far brighter than the darkness outside. As explained in Chapter 2: *Goodbye Milky Way*, the loss of the natural contrast between day and night disrupts our delicate circadian timing system, allowing the multitude of clocks in our bodies to drift apart and beat out of sync with each other like a discordant orchestra. When that happens, the body's natural defense against cancer cells and other threats, such as viruses, is disrupted, impairing the body's defenses.

By 2007, enough convincing research had accumulated for the WHO International Agency for Research on Cancer to classify circadian disruption, caused by exposure to light on the night shift, as a probable carcinogen.[16] They cited compelling evidence for significant increases in breast cancer associated with night shift work and the extensive animal studies showing that light at night disrupts the circadian system and suppresses melatonin, the cancer-protecting hormone, allowing breast cancer tumors to grow unchecked.

This shocking finding was widely publicized in the media. The Danish government started paying compensation to night shift workers who got cancer.[17] Before I knew it, the medical and safety directors of my Fortune 500 clients were calling me, asking what they should do. You have to understand that there is no way oil refineries, steel mills, nuclear power plants, or hospitals can stop their 24-hour operations, and there is no way that they could switch off the lights at night.

At that time, I didn't know what to suggest – but as you will see in Chapter 8: *Creating Healthy Light*, we have discovered the solution. It is now clear what has to be done, and what you can do to protect yourself.

The Scale of the Breast Cancer Problem

The issue goes far beyond the people who work at night. Out of the 7.6 billion people living on our planet, 2.8 billion are women with breasts (i.e., females 14 years or older), at least 80% of whom are exposed to bright electric light after dusk.[18]

The 2.1 million new breast cancer cases currently diagnosed each year in these 2.8 billion women gives us a worldwide average breast cancer diagnosis rate of 75 per 100,000 women per year.[19] This is three times higher than the 20-30 per 100,000 yearly incidence rate in women who have never seen electric light. But this 75 per 100,000 rate averages both the women in rural parts of the world who have little or no access to electric light, and the women in highly electrified regions of the world such as North America and Europe with breast cancer rates of 100 or more new cases per 100,000 women per year.

Given these numbers, we can conservatively estimate that at least half of the breast cancer cases diagnosed in the world today are linked to the widespread use of unhealthy electric light. That is over a million cases per year. We are faced with a cancer epidemic of a scale that Thomas Edison could never have envisaged.

If these women were all adequately treated, the cost would

be enormous. Treating a woman with breast cancer, with all the diagnostic tests, surgeries, chemotherapy, and radiation treatments, can total $200,000 per person.[20] Thus, the cases attributable to exposure to the wrong electric light at the wrong time could exceed $200 Billion per year. And that doesn't include the psychological and economic burden on the women with breast cancer, and their families.

The actual health care costs are, of course, somewhat less than that, because this standard of care is unfortunately not found in the more underdeveloped regions of the world, or underserved and uninsured populations in the developed world. But the psychological and family economic costs in those cases can become that much higher.

Pushback and Clarification

Faced with the enormity of these conclusions, as expected, there has been pushback. There have been a growing number of scientific studies that confirm the relationship between light at night, melatonin suppression, and the rising incidence of breast cancer, and many stories in the press reporting on these scientific findings. But the general response has been denial, especially in the $150 billion/year lighting industry, and among government regulators, since it seemed to them that nothing can be done.

One typical response is to punt the issue and say more research is needed. Yet since the WHO International Agency for Research on Cancer concluded in 2007 that night work with light exposure at night causing circadian disruption was a probable carcinogen, another $2 Billion of academic research has been conducted on circadian and light interactions.[21] This has produced over 10,000 peer-reviewed scientific articles published by over 30,000 scientists that have further cemented the conclusion that light at night is carcinogenic, as well as causing a host of other medical problems we will discuss in the next chapter.

Another response is to look for and widely publicize any study that would seem to contradict the emerging findings of light-induced breast cancer risk. After the Danish government began paying compensation to women who had developed breast cancer after working night shifts, the British government started to get pressure to compensate shift workers with cancer. In response, the UK Health and Safety Executive (HSE), the government agency responsible for workplace health, safety and welfare, commissioned a study at the University of Oxford to investigate the risk of light at night.

The findings were trumpeted widely. "Night shift work has no effect on breast cancer incidence" the published study claimed.[22] However, a closer look at this poorly designed study reveals that the 800,000 women they studied were mostly retired and elderly, and only followed for 2-3 years late in life.[23] They classified them as shift workers if they had worked only a single night shift in their lives. They ignored the fact that the light at night effect is most potent in young pre-menopausal women, and the risk develops over 5 years or more of exposure.

Since then, even more evidence has accumulated for the devastating effect of light at night exposure. In 2020, the WHO International Agency for Research on Cancer reexamined its classification of exposure to light on the night shift as a probable carcinogen. It confirmed its conclusion after taking into account all the accumulated evidence, including the flawed HSE – University of Oxford study.[24]

In the USA, the investigation of the carcinogenicity of light at night was referred to the National Toxicology Program of the National Institutes of Health. This agency had previously identified the carcinogenicity of asbestos in 1980 and smoking in 2000. Starting in 2014, they conducted a seven-year study of the evidence, leading to a published report in 2021 citing 721 scientific studies.[25] In summary, they concluded:

1. There is high confidence for a causal relationship between human cancer and frequent and long-term night shift work, especially beginning in early adulthood—that causes circadian disruption.

2. Exposure to electric light at night causes melatonin suppression and other types of circadian disruption, which lead to the proliferation and growth of breast or mammary-gland cancer in experimental animals.

3. The characteristics of electric light that are most likely to cause circadian disruption include a combination of blue-enriched light, longer duration, exposure to electric light during the biological night, and higher light intensity levels.

4. Insufficient exposure to daylight because of our indoor lifestyles also contributes to circadian disruption and cancer risk.

Shining Light on Prostate Cancer

In 2006, there I was, back in the operating room for the first time after many years, only this time I wasn't the surgeon. I was the patient. The scene was familiar, the gowns, drapes, masks and the smells, the clattering sounds from the instrument tray and the lights … but all from a very different surreal perspective.

I had developed prostate cancer, which, like breast cancer,

is highly sensitive to light exposure at night and is the second leading cause of cancer death in American men, behind only lung cancer. It is the disease that killed my best friend in medical school, the actor William Hurt, entertainer Merv Griffin, Nobel Prize winners Linus Pauling and Bernard Crick, and millions of others.

In hindsight, it was a predictable outcome of a career studying circadian rhythms and applying this science to helping people who worked shifts around the clock. I had been repeatedly exposed to lights at night as I sat with and studied oil refinery and nuclear power plant operators in their control rooms, and in the cockpit with commercial airline pilots crossing the Pacific and Atlantic, railroad engineers pushing the mile-long freight trains across the Rockies, and with the technicians and assembly line workers at countless factories in countless industries. Not to mention the many overnight research studies I conducted in the lab.

I was proactive and lucky. As soon as my routine prostate-specific antigen (PSA) test results started climbing, I went to the leading prostate surgeon in the country, Dr Patrick Walsh, at Johns Hopkins. He had achieved an impressive record of spectacular results because of his obsession with the details of diagnosis and surgery. He removed my prostate and caught my cancer early before it had spread.

Millions of people are not so lucky, and this is a disease to be taken seriously. Although less extensively studied, the evidence for the impact of electric light on the risk of prostate cancer is similar to that of breast cancer. Men who are exposed to significant amounts of light at night as they work night shifts have up to three times the incidence rate of prostate cancer.[26] And men who slept in "quite illuminated" bedrooms had a 2-3 times higher risk of prostate cancer than those who slept in the dark.[27] Furthermore, animal models of prostate cancer, like breast cancer, have established the relationship between dim indoor daytime light, blue-rich light exposure at night, melatonin suppression, circadian disruption, and increased prostate tumor growth.[28]

What About the Rest of Us?

The growth of tumors, such as breast, prostate, and colorectal cancers, is a long-term consequence of our increasing exposure to the wrong type of electric light at the wrong time of day. Notable is the dramatic rise in cancer in young people. Since blue-rich LED lights were introduced in 2015, breast cancer diagnoses in women aged 20 - 49 have been increasing by ~4% per year and gastrointestinal cancers in young people by over 2% per year.

However, because these cancers will ultimately develop in less than 20% of us, it might be tempting to take our chances amid all the other risks in our lives and carry on as usual.

But the cancer risk is only the tip of the iceberg. The misuse of electric light impacts all of us in so many other ways and degrades our health and well-being, often with immediate effect. In the next chapter, *Goodbye Milky Way*, we will explore these other serious health effects of electric light exposure that can have adverse impacts within hours or days.

In this chapter, you have learned:

1. Electric light is the "tobacco" of breast and prostate cancer, potentially accounting for the majority of cases in highly electrified countries in the developed world.

2. Hundreds of scientific studies have shown the association between electric light exposure and cancer, and the biological mechanisms by which it occurs.

3. Major scientific review panels at the World Health Organization, and the US National Institutes of Health have confirmed the carcinogenic risk of electric light.

2

Goodbye Milky Way

Our electrically illuminated lifestyles have upset the internal temporal order of our bodies and impacted our health.

For the first 10,000 generations of human existence, our ancestors stared up at night in wonderment and awe at the thousands of stars visible to the human eye and the ghostly band of light from the Milky Way stretching from horizon to horizon. But nowadays, the glow from billions of electric lights obscures the view of the night sky for most of us in the industrialized, electrified world.[29] Only when you get far away from the light pollution of cities and highways can you experience the full restorative impact of nocturnal darkness, illuminated by the beauty of the night sky. And, sadly these days, most people never get to see the full majesty of the Milky Way.

That outdoor existence of years past also exposed our ancestors to bright light during the day and the precise regularity of sunset and sunrise governed by the Earth's seasonal rotation around the sun. But electric light now permits us to stay indoors, away from

Electric light pollution obscures the view of the night sky and Milky Way that our ancestors enjoyed for over 10,000 generations.
(Adapted from iStock.com/Ivan Boryshchak (Left) and nukleerkedi (Right))

windows during the daytime hours, and stay awake working or playing late into the evening irrespective of the season of the year. Because of all this convenience at a flick of a switch, the average person today spends less than 8% of their time outdoors exposed to natural levels of lighting.[30]

Indoor lighting levels under electric light are dramatically different than those outside in the natural world. You can use a simple device, a lux meter such as photographers use, to measure the intensity of light. Outside on a cloudy, overcast day, you are exposed to about 10,000 lux of light, and when it is sunny, light levels can rise to 50,000 to 100,000 lux. After sunset the light levels drop precipitously to 0.0001 lux (less than one-thousandth of a lux) on a dark cloudy night and 0.2 lux (one-fifth of a lux) under the brightest light of a full moon.[31] But indoors, whether it is day or night, we get only 50 – 500 lux of illumination from our electric lights because much more than that creates discomfort and eyestrain from glare and reflections. Hence, we mostly live indoors in a constant twilight of electric light that is typically 1,000 times dimmer during the day than natural sunlight and 1,000 times brighter after dusk than even the brightest moonlight.

Our losses from being indoors are thus far greater than missing the full beauty of nature. The impact on the human body of becoming untethered from the natural day-night cycle is profound. Even those of us living seemingly innocuous regular lives, sleeping at night and working indoors during the day, are disrupted by the electric light from lamps and display screens. Not to mention the harm our outdoor lighting does to all other species of flora and fauna, as discussed in Chapter 12: *Light Pollution and Biodiversity*.

Recreating the Days and Nights of Our Past

But how different could today's life be from the days before Edison? To find out, Dr. Kenneth Wright, a Professor at the University of Colorado, Boulder, recreated the lighting conditions of the bygone pre-electric era in the summer of 2012 by taking groups of male and female volunteers into the Cache la Poudre Wilderness deep in the backwoods of the Rocky Mountains, west of Fort Collins.[32] He had them spend a week without flashlights, electronics, cell phones, or any other electric light source. They could have a campfire as our ancestors did, but nothing electrical.

Before the camping trips, as a baseline, he recorded each volunteer in their everyday living environment for a week. They all lived typical lives, sleeping at night, with some early risers and others late evening types. Dr. Wright's team used portable devices to constantly monitor each person's levels of light exposure throughout the day and night, the timing of their self-selected sleep, and also measured the timing of their melatonin production – a marker of the timing of the internal circadian clock.

Living without electric devices enables us to experience a bygone life in tune with nature's rhythms. (iStock.com/anatoliy_gleb)

These measurements continued as they hiked into the wilderness, leaving electrical civilization behind. Each individual hiked as they chose during the day, sat around campfires in the evenings, retired to their tents to sleep, and woke whenever they chose on their own personal schedule.

When these camping trips were taken in the summer, with 14-hour days and 10-hour nights, the timing of sleep and the melatonin rhythms shifted two hours earlier under the natural light-dark cycle, but they woke up much more alert in the mornings because their internal circadian clocks had become fully synchronized to natural nighttime. When the outdoor camping trips were repeated in the winter, with 10-hour days and 14-hour nights, they fell asleep two and a half hours earlier in the evening and woke at the same time so that they slept for about two and a half hours longer each night. Their exposure to much brighter daytime light levels and natural darkness at night caused their sleep timing and melatonin production in both summer and winter seasons to become tightly synchronized to the natural day-night cycle.[33]

But this story gets even more interesting when you look at the difference between the campers who were morning larks (people who naturally rise early and are at their best early in the day) versus those campers who were evening owls (individuals who find it harder to get up in the morning but are at their most productive late in the evening). When exposed to the much brighter outdoor light levels during the day, and the absence of electric light at night, those campers who were natural morning types and those who were evening types all synchronized to the same natural day-night cycle, almost erasing the significant differences seen when they were at home living with electrical illumination. This suggests that the morning-evening differences in individual sleep-wake cycles are because some people are much more sensitive to lack of daylight and exposure to evening electric light than others. Some people get shifted a lot by evening light, and their sleep can get seriously disrupted. Others are more impervious to evening light and have their sleep shifted less. These differences matter because people who go to sleep late, and are exposed to more light in the evenings, have a higher risk of obesity and diabetes.

From these studies it was clear that electric light has profoundly changed our orientation to both day and night, not only with respect to the time we sleep, but also the internal timing mechanisms of our bodies. We are no longer tightly in step with the Earth's daily 24-hour rotation on its axis, or with the Earth's yearly rotation around the sun. The invention of electric light has caused our body rhythms to be no longer tightly synchronized to the rhythms of the universe.

Even More Electric Light at Night.
Even More Disease.

Sleeping at night with the lights on is surprisingly common. Surveys show that 40% or more adults do this regularly, often because of anxiety.[34] Even in a single night of sleeping with the lights on, fundamental aspects of our physiology are changed. Even in young, healthy people, the fight or flight sympathetic nervous system response is activated, heart rate is increased, and a pre-diabetic state of insulin resistance develops by the morning.[35]

Sleeping with the lights on almost doubles obesity, diabetes & hypertension risk.(iStock.com/bernardbodo)

The long-term effects of leaving the lights on in the bedroom at night are serious. A study of 552 elderly Chicago residents, aged 63 – 84, living in their homes, with continuously measured light levels, found that 54% of them slept each night with the lights on.[36] Those people who left the lights on in the bedroom had almost twice the rate of obesity, diabetes and high blood pressure compared to the other elderly people in the study who slept in the dark. Other studies have shown, besides obesity and diabetes, that mood disorders and depression are more common when people leave the lights on at night.[37]

Even more significant effects are seen in the more than 20 million people in the US, and over 60 million worldwide, who work overnight shifts in health care, manufacturing, transportation, oil and gas, and other 24/7 industries. They are often exposed to bright lights all night long, and for multiple consecutive night shifts. Their sleep is disrupted by their rotating or extended work schedules, so they are constantly fatigued. Over the long term, they suffer much higher rates of diseases associated with circadian disruption, including obesity, diabetes, and heart disease.[38]

I got to experience this world first-hand in my first year after medical school as a junior surgeon working 36-hour shifts under bright hospital lights, with 12 hours off between shifts, and then back in for another 36 hours. The extreme disruption of my circadian rhythms, fragmented sleep, and perpetual malaise rendered me into a near constant state of exhaustion and brain fog where I sometimes couldn't make sense of the prescriptions I had just written, and led me on more than one occasion, as I mentioned in the Introduction, to nod off in the operating room.

My experience was so aptly captured by the song by Melanie that was constantly playing on the radio that year:

Look what they've done to my brain, ma
Look at what they've done to my brain
Well, they picked it like a chicken bone
And I think that I'm half insane, ma
Look what they've done to my song.

What Have They Done to My Song, Ma? Written by Melanie Safka, *with permission.*

That year had such an impact on me that I decided to take a detour from my surgical career, and to pursue a Ph.D. in Physiology at Harvard Medical School to study circadian rhythms. This research field was, at that time, very new and unexplored. Only three scientific papers on the impact of light on circadian rhythms had been published in the year before I entered medical school. I was warned in 1971 by Professor Richard Wurtman, a leading neuroscientist at MIT, not to risk my career on circadian rhythms as they were caused by the daily rotation of the Earth, and no one had shown that animals or humans had internal biological clocks. Fortunately, I ignored his advice and got myself a front-row seat in this field's extraordinary growth which now produces thousands of scientific research articles per year.

What is Circadian Disruption?

When I started my PhD in Physiology at Harvard in 1971, very little was known about circadian clocks. I wanted to understand what was causing all that malaise and dysfunction that I had experienced when my work and sleep schedule became dissociated from the natural 24-hour cycle of day and night. I had already traveled across the Atlantic from England to North America by ocean liner, and airplane, and had experienced the aptly named jet-lag with its sleep disruption, brain fog and malaise after flying, but not after traveling by ship, across the same five time zones.

One key difference is the rate of adjustment. On the ocean liner it took nine days to cover 3,200 miles; on the plane less than nine hours. I still remember my Atlantic Ocean crossing. It was only after the first day at sea, when we had yet to pass

Penzance, the most westerly town in England, that I realized how slow the ship was going. We were travelling 3,200 miles at a speed of 15 miles per hour, taking two days to cross each time zone. Each evening, my shipmates and I stayed up half an hour later, dancing to the ship's orchestra. When I finally stepped onto the American shore, I felt perfectly normal with no jet-lag, my body perfectly in tune with the local time zone.

My research at Harvard showed that the various physiological systems in the body (heart, liver, kidneys etc,) each had their own circadian clocks which were usually all tightly synchronized via hormonal and neural circadian signals.[39] But when the 24- hour light-dark cycle was disrupted, either by continually leaving the lights on, or shifting the daily timing of light and dark, the different body systems drifted out of sync. For example, the timing of sleep might adjust to a time zone shift in a couple of days, but it would take a week or more for the kidney clocks to catch up. As a result, someone like me, in my younger days, who normally slept through the night, would have to get up and go to the bathroom a couple of times in the middle of the night, for a few days after crossing the Atlantic.

The best analogy is an orchestra, where the conductor usually keeps the instrument players in sync with his baton. But if the orchestra can no longer see, or ignores, the conductor the different players can get out of sync and create a discordant sound. The human body is a very precisely timed machine with the timing of the individual circadian rhythms in all its cells in synchrony. When they get out of sync, circadian disruption occurs.

Circadian disruption is often much more serious than the inconvenience of going to the bathroom in the middle of the night. Fundamental body systems like thermoregulation can fail, so the body no longer can keep warm when room temperature falls.[40] Metabolism malfunctions so that individuals gain weight and develop diabetes.[41] Blood pressure regulation can fail, so that patients with disrupted circadian rhythms under the continuous lighting conditions of the ICU have longer hospital stays and higher death rates.[42] And long-term circadian disruption is associated with reduced life expectancy in animal research studies and in people with irregular sleep wake cycles.[43]

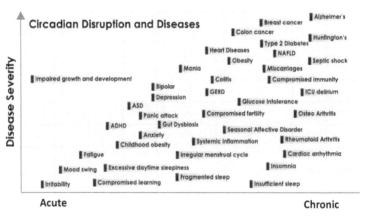

A broad range of impairments and diseases are linked to circadian disruption. (Adapted from Sulli et al (2018) Trends Pharmacol. Science with permission.)

The effects of living under constant twilight year-round with limited exposure to natural light and dark may also have broader implications for human reproduction. In 1860, in the pre-Edison era, the average age that girls reached menarche (the first occurrence of menstruation) was 16-17 years.[44] Nowadays, with abundant electric light and the constant use of smartphones, the average teenage girl reaches menarche at 12-13 years. Furthermore, births used to be seasonal, like other animal species, varying up to 60% by time of year.[45] That seasonal aspect of human reproduction has now been lost. We do not understand the mechanism behind all these changes, but it raises serious questions about the widespread impact of our use of electric light.

Locating the Human Circadian Clock

When I first joined the Harvard Medical School faculty in 1975 as an assistant professor of physiology, there was a big gap in knowledge about human circadian rhythms. Even though humans had circadian rhythms that could be disrupted by travel across time zones and working night shifts, it was firmly believed that humans were quite different from other animals. There was no evidence of a SCN circadian master clock in the human brain, and experiments by the leading circadian scientists at the Max Planck Institute in Germany, Jurgen Aschoff and Rutger Wever, led them to believe that human circadian rhythms were not synchronized by the 24-hour light-dark cycle like all other species, but instead by some complex form of social interaction.[46]

My Harvard appointment allowed me to build a Laboratory for Circadian Physiology at Harvard Medical School and recruit a brilliant team of graduate students and postdocs, most of whom went on to become professors at leading universities. With this dedicated team, we made huge strides forward in the uncharted territory of circadian clocks.

 SCIENTIFIC ASIDE: Circadian Clocks

The master circadian clock in the brains of hamsters and rats was not discovered until 1972, a year after my conversation with Professor Wurtman.[47] It is a pair of tiny pinhead-sized clusters of nerve cells in the hypothalamus of the brain called the supra-chiasmatic nucleus (abbreviated "SCN"). This SCN master clock receives information about the timing of day and night from special receptors in the eye called "intrinsically photosensitive retinal ganglion cells" (ipRGC) that detect illumination levels in the outdoor or indoor environment, but, unlike rods and cones, do not communicate the visual images we see. These retinal ganglion cells communicate the illumination information to the SCN via a special bundle of nerve fibers called the retino-hypothalmic tract. When the SCN clock is destroyed in these or-dinarily nocturnal animals, they lose their sense of night and day, and their activity and feeding become scattered randomly across day and night. It would take another eight years before we could show that humans also had a SCN master clock in the brain.

One key set of discoveries came when one of my students, Charles ("Chuck") Czeisler, helped persuade Dr Elliot Weitzman, a leading sleep specialist and Chief of Neurology at the Albert Einstein College of Medicine to convert the top floor of the Montefiore Hospital in New York into a Laboratory for Human Chronophysiology. Here, in collaboration with our team at Harvard, we could finally answer the question – was the human circadian clock synchronized by light? By creating a living space totally isolated from all time cues, we were able to show that the daily light-dark cycle was the most powerful synchronizer of human circadian rhythms.[48] However, in the absence of a 24-hour day-night cycle, the human circadian system drifted progressively out of sync with the clock on the wall, and could separate into multiple free-running rhythms.

But there was a missing piece of the puzzle. Did humans also have a master circadian clock, like monkeys and all other animal species? The official brain atlases, that documented slice by slice all the various nuclei and nerve bundles of the human brain, showed no evidence of anything resembling a SCN clock. The key insight came when one of my post docs, Ralph Lydic, discovered that the brain atlases with pictures of thin slices of the human brain, displayed only every fiftieth slice, and threw away the 49 slices in between. Since the SCN clock is very small it was entirely possible that it had been missed or inconsistently seen, and therefore ignored. When Ralph went back to look at all the other 49 slices, lo and behold there was the human SCN, positioned similarly to the monkey SCN, in the hypothalamus of the human brain.[49]

SCIENTIFIC ASIDE:
Resetting the Circadian Clock

The signals from the ipRGC illumination detectors in the eye adjust the SCN master clock either forwards or backwards each day, to keep us in sync with the daily light- dark cycle. Light in the evening delays the SCN clock, whereas light in the morning advances the timing of the clock. So, if you fly westward from Boston to San Francisco, for example, your eyes detect more light in the evening, and the SCN clock is gradually shifted westward so that your clock becomes synchronized to California time. The reverse happens when you fly eastward from San Francisco to Boston. After you arrive in

Boston the natural dawn occurs 3 hours earlier, and the extra morning light shifts your clock eastwards until you get back in sync.[50]

But there are two problems. First, the SCN master clock can only be shifted by an hour or two each day, so it takes several days to adjust to a flight across multiple time zones. And second, many of the circadian clocks in the other organs and cells of the body take even longer to adjust, so the various systems of the body become out of sync with each other, and this creates the state of malaise and brain fog we call "circadian disruption".

By 1983, we were able to put this whole story together in 75 peer-reviewed scientific articles, and a book, *The Clocks That Time Us: Physiology of the Circadian Timing System*, published by Harvard University Press, which served as the textbook for this new field for many years.[51]

What We Did Not Know

But there were some fundamental things we did not understand at that time.

First, we did not know how biological clocks inside cells could measure time so precisely and reliably. That took a series of major advances in molecular biology and genetics to identify the multiple intracellular components and learn how they interacted to create a circadian clock that precisely generated approximately 24-hour circadian rhythms. Leading that effort were Professors Jeffrey Hall, Michael Rosbash and Michael Young who won the 2017 Nobel Prize in Physiology or Medicine for their work.[52]

Second, we did not know at that time about the central role of melatonin, a hormone produced by the pineal gland, in signaling that it was dark outside to the cells and organs throughout the body. We now know it is a key part of the hormonal and nervous signals that normally keep all the circadian clocks in the body beating in sync. However, when melatonin is suppressed by electric light the timing signal is lost and circadian disruption occurs. As discussed in Chapter 1, melatonin triggers many cellular repairing processes, including suppressing cancer cells in the body, that occur during nighttime hours.[53] When it was first discovered that the timing of melatonin production overlaps the timing of sleep, melatonin was referred to as the "sleep hormone" in the popular press. It has since become clear that, at the normal levels seen in the human body, melatonin does not cause sleepiness, although large pharmacological doses can make you sleepy.[54] Melatonin's central role is to serve as a signal of biological night, which helps keep all the cells in the body in sync with the light-dark cycle, whether it is natural day or night, or distorted by the use of electric light.

The third and most surprising discovery was the role of the blue wavelengths in white light in signaling day and night, as we will discuss next in Chapter 3: *Clockwork Blue*. It is also the most significant scientific breakthrough as it provides a way out of our dilemma with electric light – how to enjoy the benefits of light at our fingertips without causing harm to our health.

The world has lost so much because of the indiscriminate use of electric light. Seduced by the convenience of the light switch we have not been very smart about the types of lights we use, when we use them, and how we protect our health and the environment. But as you will see the core science has been done and proven solutions have been developed. We don't have to return to the "dark ages" before electric light. By the time you finish this book, you will have a road map to regaining much of what you have lost, without losing the gift of having attractive light always available at the flick of a switch.

In this chapter, you have learned:

1. When we use electric light indoors, we are living in a state of constant twilight as compared to the brightness of outdoor daylight and the darkness of even a moonlit night.

2. In the absence of the natural day-night cycle the precisely timed circadian clocks in our body drift out of sync with each other so we live in a state of circadian disruption making us much more vulnerable to illness and disease.

3. The greater the light exposure at night, the greater the risk of serious illnesses such as obesity, diabetes, heart disease, and breast and prostate cancer.

3

Clockwork Blue

Blue light has been the key day-night signal ever since life began deep in the oceans.

The light that illuminates us, whether it is sunlight, electric light, or a candle, is composed of a rainbow mix of colors that fuse to form the white or yellowish color we normally observe. We only get to see the beautiful array of the separated colors of the rainbow when sunlight falls on a piece of crystal, or raindrops in the sky. Then we get to admire the violet, blue, green, yellow, orange and red hidden in the visible light spectrum.

In the 1980's at Harvard, when we located the master circadian clock in the human brain, and showed that was synchronized by daily light-dark cycles, as I discussed in Chapter 2: *Goodbye Milky Way*, we assumed that any visible light would be effective.[55] At that time, it never occurred to us that only a narrow part of the light spectrum, a sky-blue color, would be responsible for synchronizing circadian clocks to the Earth's 24-hour daily rotation. Nor did we realize that this sky-blue color would enable us to identify which electric lights are unhealthy, or make it possible to create healthy lighting solutions.

The Deep Blue Sea

How did sky-blue become the critical time-of-day signal? We must go back to the history of early life deep in the oceans, half a billion years ago. Many of the basic cellular systems and biochemical pathways our bodies rely on today evolved in the highly competitive "survival of the fittest" world in the primitive oceans during the Cambrian Period (542-488 million years ago).[56] The oceans were the womb of evolution, and the conditions within that womb shaped the genesis of our evolutionary ancestors.

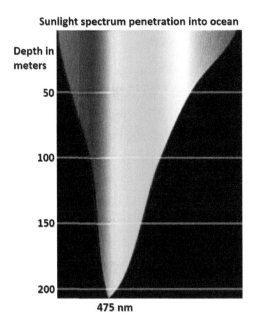

Sunlight spectrum penetration into ocean

Depth in meters

50

100

150

200

475 nm

The penetration of the color spectrum of sunlight at different depths in the open ocean. (Courtesy of Kyle Carothers, NOAA-OE)

One curious law of nature in those Cambrian oceans, and our oceans today, is that the sea water absorbs all the rainbow colors of the sunlight spectrum, except for sky-blue. So, the violet, green, yellow, orange, and red components of the sunlight shining on the oceans do not penetrate the ocean depths. If you go below 200 meters (660 feet), all you see is blue light when it is daytime and pitch darkness when it is night.[57]

In the predator-eat-prey struggle to survive there was constant danger from those creatures immediately above you in the food chain. Being able to predict when and where food would be available, and when and where you might become food yourself, was a huge advantage. Detecting the sky-blue color of ocean light was crucial for determining whether it was day or night, and whether one should hide or hunt for food. Those life forms that developed sky-blue light receptors gained an evolutionary advantage and lived to survive and multiply.

A view of a mussel bed near New Zealand at 100 meters depth, lit only by the blue wavelengths in sunlight that penetrate to that depth. (Image courtesy of the New Zealand-American NOAA vents program)

But even better was the ability to predict dawn and dusk so you could have enough time to head for the feeding grounds, or scurry for shelter from predators, before the day became night, or night became day. It was not healthy, or compatible with species survival, to be caught in the wrong place at the wrong time. Those life forms that developed circadian clocks synchronized by their sky-blue light receptors to the precise 24-hour cycle of day and night, gained a massive advantage.[58] They could tuck away in their safe hiding places long before the sun sank below the horizon, or arose in the morning, depending on whether their survival game plan was nocturnal or day-active.

As life forms became multicellular and more complex, internal signaling of day and night to all the cells of the body became critical, so one more fundamental component evolved, which we see in virtually all animals today. This was the chemical molecule we call melatonin, which serves as the darkness hormone[59] Even the body cells which could not see light were informed when it was dark outside by a surge in melatonin production, and that it was light outside by suppressed levels of melatonin.

Even in simple single-celled creatures living in our oceans today, we can see the fundamental blue-sensitive clockwork. For example, Gonyaulux, the algae responsible for the toxic red tide, has all within its single cell, the fundamental apparatus of sky-blue detector, circadian clock, and melatonin darkness signaling[60] And in most other more complex animals in sea, land, and air, including we human beings, this half-billion-year-old timing apparatus keeps life synchronized to the daily progression of light and dark on our consistently spinning planet.

Blue Sky Thinking

As life emerged from the oceans onto land and became exposed to the full rainbow array of colors embedded in sunlight, you might think there might no longer be an advantage to using blue as the circadian clock timing signal. Plenty of other colors in sunlight could indicate the difference between night and day. However, two curious features of physics provide an advantage to using blue as the circadian time clue, even when living a terrestrial life.

Not only is there more blue in sunlight than other colors, but blue light behaves differently. When sunlight hits our atmosphere, the blue rays of light hit the particles, molecules, and aerosols floating in the sky and briefly excites them. The blue energy is immediately released and scattered, which is called the Rayleigh effect, named after Lord Rayleigh, the British mathematician and winner of the 1904 Nobel Prize in Physics.[61] Blue is scattered much more than the other colors in sunlight which is why we see the sky as blue.[62] And this blue color of the Rayleigh sky is amazingly close to the narrow spectrum of blue that penetrates the ocean depths. The blue color indicating daytime was thus biologically familiar as our evolutionary ancestors emerged from the ocean onto land.

Blue Hour

But the story gets even better. There is a mystical time just before dawn, and just after dusk, called the blue hour. It is featured in paintings and in photography, in literature, and folklore.[63] It is even memorialized in L'Heure Bleue, a famous French perfume created by Jacques Guerlain in 1912. The perfume, a "velvety soft and romantic" fragrance was claimed by Guerlain to evoke the "bluish dusk and anticipation of night before the first stars appear in the sky".[64]

The blue hour is not actually an hour, it is usually closer to 20 minutes in length.[65] For example, at the two seasons of the year when the sun sets at 6 pm, the "blue hour" lasts from 6:10 pm to 6:30 pm in the evening when the sun is 4-8 degrees below the horizon, and similarly lasts from 5:30 am to 5:50 am in the morning before the sun rises at 6 am. This "blue hour" tracks

The "blue hour" just after the sun has set below the horizon. (iStock.com/ HABesen)

dawn and dusk according to the local latitude and longitude with the seasons of the year.

Why does the sky turn deep blue after the sun falls below the horizon in the evening and again before the sun rises at dawn? It is not the Rayleigh light scattering effect, as that would predict the sky would become grey. Instead, it is an entirely different phenomenon, called the Chappius effect.[66] James Chappius was a French chemist who discovered that ozone, which is concentrated in a layer about 15 miles above the Earth's surface, acts as a color filter.[67] Ozone absorbs the yellow, orange, and red parts of the light spectrum but lets the blue light pass through, creating the deep blue sky during the blue hour. Having a 20-minute pulse of blue light that anticipates dawn, and being able to detect it with specialized blue receptors, reinforced the value of retaining the half-billion-year-old blue clockwork.

Thus, three entirely independent laws of physics, seawater light absorption, Rayleigh light scattering and Chappius ozone light filtering, all conspire to provide the critical blue signal that indicates the time of day to the life forms on our rotating planet.

 ## SCIENTIFIC ASIDE: Rhythm and Blues

The clockwork blue system in humans was not elucidated until more recently. In 2000, the specialized ipRGC illumination detectors in our eyes, that we discussed in Chapter 2 *Goodbye Milky Way*, were discovered to contain a photopigment called melanopsin which is highly sensitive to sky-blue light.[68] These melanopsin-containing ipRGC illumination detectors transmit information about the presence or absence of sky-blue light directly to the circadian clock in the suprachiasmatic nucleus (SCN) by the retinal-hypothalmic tract.[69] In turn, the SCN signals the time of day via nerve pathways to the pineal gland, and synchronizes the release of the melatonin hormone darkness signal to help keep all the cells of our body aware of when it is dark outside.[70]

These ipRGC sky-blue light receptors have a peak sensitivity at 479 nm, and are quite distinct from

> the rods and cones that enable our vision.[71] In fact, some people who are visually blind still have the melanopsin system intact so their circadian clocks remain synchronized to day and night.[72]

The rods are the receptors in our eyes that give us vision in dim twilight or moonlight at night after our eyes have become accustomed to the dark – a process called dark adaptation. The ability to sense all the beautiful colors of nature in daylight, or a painting or photograph in a well-lit room, is delivered by the cones. These cones come in three color sensitivity types, violet (420nm), green (534nm) and yellow (564nm) which send their signals to the visual cortex of our brains where our remarkable awareness of nature's color palate is reassembled in our internal perception metaverse.[73] These rods and cones enable our vision. In contrast the ipRGC sky-blue receptors do not provide any visual image perception, but quietly inform our circadian clocks of the time of day without us ever being consciously aware of their powerful regulation of our brain and body.

Conquering the Night

When our artificial light sources emit any sky-blue light in their spectrum at night we are messing with Mother Nature, or the biological world order. And we are quite unaware of what we are doing. We cannot see with our eyes how much sky-blue a white light bulb is emitting. We just see it as white light without being aware of the spectral rainbow of colors that make up that light.

When our human ancestors first gained control of fire about 250,000 years ago, they mostly burned wood which fortunately for them emits very little sky-blue color in its yellowish-reddish flames.[74] When candles were first invented

3,000 years ago they also emitted very little sky-blue light in their yellowish flame.[75] Not only that, but the levels of lighting were very dim by today's standards. So, for all intents and purposes, the natural sky-blue signals of day and night were undisturbed by the invention of fire and flame.

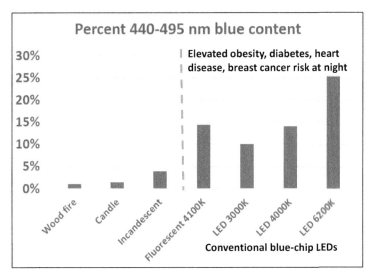

Circadian sky blue (440-495 nm) content of different light sources as percentage of total visible light (380-780nm). Fluorescent and blue-chip LED lights, because of their high blue content, can be harmful when used in the evening or at night. (Copyright Circadian Light Research Center)

Thomas Edison's invention of the incandescent filament light bulb delivered much more sky-blue light at night than humans had ever seen. The effect was tempered by Edison's choice of an incandescent filament which mimicked the color of the candlelight to which his initial customers were accustomed. Even so, about 4% of the total visible light emitted was the circadian sky-blue color that disrupts our circadian clocks, compared to only 1% blue for fire and 1.5% blue for candlelight.[76] That may not seem like a much greater percentage of blue light, but it also matters how bright the light is, and electric lights were much brighter than candles or gas lamps.

Appetite for Light

Our appetites, whether it is for sugar, salt, or anything else our bodies crave, when taken to excess, are not good for our health, and so it is with light. Turning up the electric lights at night allows us to enhance the beauty of our indoor surroundings, and who wouldn't want that? It also enables us to do detailed work and hobbies uninhibited by the available illumination. So, the flick-of-switch availability of cheap electric illumination triggered our appetite for bright light after the sun had set. As a result, for the first time in human history, the total amount of sky-blue light that reached our eyes after dark (total visible light intensity multiplied by 440-495 nm blue percentage) was increased to higher levels than was good for human health.

But we couldn't stop there. The momentum of progress, and the desire for more beautiful light, drove human ingenuity to create whiter, brighter, and more energy efficient lights. Fluorescent lights were first widely introduced in the 1950s and instead of the 4% blue content of incandescent bulbs they delivered 10-15% sky blue.[77] Most office buildings, hospitals, and schools today are still lit by fluorescent lights bathing us indiscriminately with sky-blue enriched light whether it is day, evening or night.

Growing awareness of climate change and global warming provided the incentive for the next revolution in lighting technology. The incandescent light bulb was deemed wasteful, converting 88% of the electricity it used into infrared heat, and only 12% into visible light.[78] Fluorescent lights did significantly better, delivering up to 90 lumens of light per watt of electricity as compared to only about 15 lumens per watt for incandescent light bulbs.[79] But the biggest breakthrough has come with the invention of the LED (light-emitting diode) which can deliver up to 200 lumens per watt, and now accounts for over 80% of lighting sales.[80] But these LEDs deliver up to 20-25% blue content.[81]

The LED Revolution

Alfred Nobel, the inventor of dynamite, was very conscious of how inventions could have both good and bad consequences. He bequeathed his considerable fortune to create the Nobel "prizes to those who...have conferred the greatest benefit to humankind" in physics, chemistry, medicine or physiology, literature, and peace.[82] Most of the time the Nobel Prize committee that awards these prizes has got it right, but there are exceptions. For example, in 1948, a Swiss scientist, Paul Müller, was awarded the Nobel Prize in Physiology or Medicine "for his discovery of the high efficiency of DDT as a contact poison against" insects, beetles, and mosquitos.[83] But DDT proved to be so deadly that it indiscriminately poisoned wildlife and the environment, as Rachel Carson showed in her famous book "*Silent Spring*", which ultimately led to DDT being banned by international treaty.[84]

Two Nobel prizes awarded in 2014 and 2017 illustrate how a breakthrough in physics can wreak medical havoc. In 2014 the Nobel Prize for Physics was awarded to three Japanese scientists, Isamu Akasaki, Hiroshi Amano, and Shuji Nakamura for inventing the blue-pump LED light.[85] By using crystals of Gallium Nitride (GaN) they showed that electricity could be converted into blue light with enormous efficiency, and that the blue light could be converted into white light by coating the GaN die with phosphors that absorbed blue and emitted the other colors required to form white light. But even with the phosphor coating, these LED light chips emit a spike of blue light, which is not a problem during the day but can be devastatingly harmful to human health at night.

The genetic molecular mechanisms of how circadian clocks keep time, and how they can be disrupted by blue light, were the breakthrough that led to the 2017 Nobel Prize in Physiology or Medicine to Jeffrey Hall, Michael Rosbash, and Michael Young.[86] The delicate feedback loop that enables each cell in the body to keep time and keep synchronized to the 24-hour Earth's rotation, revealed what it means to be messing with Mother Nature by the indiscriminate use of blue-pump LED lights. And indiscriminate we have been.

Their sales took off, once LEDs could be produced cheaply in mass quantities. In 2013, LEDs comprised only 1% of lighting sales, but by 2023, LEDs were in over 70% of all lights sold worldwide.[87] The existing installed base of lighting is, of course, much bigger than the yearly sales, but at this rate LEDs will replace most lights on our planet within a few years.

The problem is the blue pump in most LED lights. This is not a issue during the day, but after sunset, when we most desire electric light, blue pump LEDs disrupt circadian clocks, suppress melatonin, and cause the wide range of health disorders we have discussed, such as obesity, diabetes, heart disease, and certain cancers.

In contrast to DDT, which is toxic at all times of day, the blue pump LED is only toxic at night, and may be somewhat helpful during the day. So, it is not the blue content per se that is the problem; it is the time of day you are exposed to blue.

Blue-pump LEDs are ubiquitous. They are in light bulbs and light fixtures. They provide beautiful white screens for our computers, and TVs. They emit blue-rich light from our mobile phones and gadgets, and the clocks in our bedrooms. Their blue rays in the evening hours delay and disrupt our sleep, suppress the release of the protective melatonin hormone, and disrupt our circadian clocks.

LED lights have been heavily promoted by the US Department of Energy and by utility companies. The energy discounts they offer can defray much of the cost of replacing traditional lights and installing LEDs.[88] In the political response to global warming, you can understand the single-minded push to replace all lights with LEDs, and the temptation to ignore the health risks exacerbated by these same LEDs. After all, the energy savings on your utility bill can be easily measured, whereas it is harder to quantify the less immediate medical risks in dollar terms.

Pushback and False Claims

As public awareness of the adverse health consequences of blue-enriched LED lights has developed, spurred by reports from the American Medical Association (AMA), the World Health Organization, and the NIH National Toxicology Program, the demands for action have increased.[89] The AMA mainly focused on LEDs in streetlights, which beam harsh white, blue-rich light into peoples' homes during the nighttime hours, citing not only cancer risks but also diabetes, obesity, and reproductive effects. Furthermore, the lights we use outdoors have huge disruptive effects on animals and plants, and their reproduction and survival, as I will discuss in Chapter 12: *Light Pollution and Biodiversity*.

Unfortunately, the debate has focused on the correlated color temperature (CCT) of the light rather than its blue content. By adjusting the phosphor mix, lighting manufacturers can create relatively yellower light, which gives the *appearance* that they are addressing the problem. But the critical sky-blue content changes relatively little as lights are reduced in color temperature from 5000K (harsh white) to 3000K (softer yellowish white). The AMA panel has pushed for streetlights of less than 3000K, which quite frankly was the wrong ask. It may bring down the percentage of blue from 15% to 10%, but that is still way too much sky-blue circadian clock-disrupting light.

The focus on CCT (correlated color temperature) has given the lighting industry a seemingly easy, but false, way out. Some manufacturers incorrectly label low CCT lights as 'circadian" without any medical proof or evidence. They use a process called color-tuning, where the lights are changed from high CCT during the day to low CCT at night. But unless they transition to very low CCT values (less than 1800K) they still pump out a lot of blue-rich light during the evening and night hours.

As we will discuss in Chapter 8: *Creating Healthy Light*, lights can be, and have been, developed which protect circadian clocks and strengthen circadian rhythms, but that is not by changing CCT. Rather, it is by a process called spectral engineering validated by evidence-based medical science.

Unhealthy Screens

Starting in 2014, the headlines read "*Your phone is making you fat!*"; "*Blue light from smartphone screens linked to weight gain*", and "*Blue light from smartphones linked to some cancers*".[90] The scientific reports of the medical effects of mobile screen usage were devastating news for Apple, Samsung, and other mobile device vendors, threatening their $450 billion/year business and sending them into a panic.[91]

We spend a lot of time in the evenings staring at our computers and mobile screens, which look beautifully white but achieve that whiteness by emitting too much sky-blue light. So, the growing awareness of the harmful effects of blue-rich light at night was a threat. In response to this news, Apple introduced "Night Shift", Samsung "Blue Light Filter" and Amazon "Blue Shade".[92] In reality, these heavily marketed "fixes" change the visible background color on the screen to yellow without removing enough of the blue light. Studies of the effects of using Apple's Night Shift mode in the evening, as would be expected, show no benefits in improved sleep.

These largely cosmetic color changes to the appearance of screens or light sources are not an adequate solution, and risk lulling the user into a false sense of comfort. The irresponsible claims made by companies marketing color-tuning lights with small changes in CCT as "circadian" need to be called out as false and misleading. There needs to be a higher standard of evidence-based science before claims are made about circadian lighting, as we will discuss in the next section.

The upside of discovering the blue signal is that we now understand the cause of the health problems with electric light at night. Furthermore, as we will discuss in Chapter 8: *Creating Healthy Light*, it has also opened the door to engineering lighting solutions that provide rich sky-blue light during the day and blue-depleted light at night to protect and enhance our circadian rhythms and our health.

In this chapter, you have learned:

1. Since life began on this planet, a band of blue wavelengths has been the signal for day and night that keeps our circadian clocks synchronized to the Earth's 24-hour rotation.

2. Switching on bright blue-rich electric light at night from lamps, computer screens, and mobile phones provides a misleading blue signal which confuses our circadian clocks and disrupts our health.

3. The widespread promotion of blue-pump LEDs has delivered cheap bright light, but at an enormous cost for human health and well-being.

4

Human-Light Interaction

Each of the rainbow colors in sunlight has specific effects on our health, which may be missing in the artificial spectra of electric lights.

Colorless tiny packets of energy that Albert Einstein named "photons" stream out of the sun traveling at the speed of light, and reaching the Earth's surface 8 minutes later.[93] Every light photon that reaches the surface of the Earth provides warmth, but fewer than half of the trillions of photons, that arrive each fraction of a second at the human eye, can be detected as visible light.[94] Most of the remaining photons that the human eye cannot see are infrared light, and the remaining 8% are ultraviolet light.

Amazing interactions occur between humans and visible light photons when they penetrate the human eye and reach the retina. Some photons arriving directly from the sky, or reflected off objects in our surroundings, are perceived visually as colors. Others trigger responses in the retina that don't involve

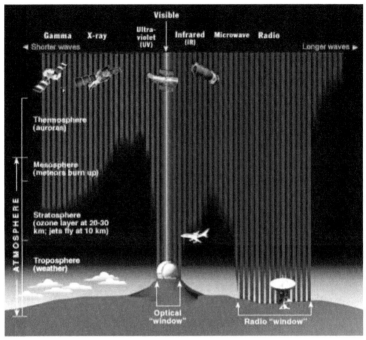

Light is defined as the narrow band of UV, visible, and IR radiation that reaches the Earth's surface in the optical window. Most other radiation, except for radio waves, is absorbed by the Earth's atmosphere.
(Credit: OpenStax, Rice University, modification of work by STScI/JHU/ NASA)

visual images. These include adjusting the size of the pupil to regulate the amount of light entering the eye, and automatically synchronizing our circadian clocks with day and night, as we discussed in Chapter 3: Clockwork Blue.[95] An abundance of visible light photons, when we are walking outdoors in nature during the day, calms our fears and anxieties by downregulating the amygdala in our brain, and their absence at night triggers our amygdala-driven fear of the dark.[96] There are also responses to light photons reaching our skin that are non-visual, and do not involve the eyes. Our response to each of these individual photons depends on their energy and wavelength.

Before we discuss the creation of healthy electric light in the next section of this book, it is worth understanding the challenges we face when we replace natural sunlight with electric light. Electric light sources such as light bulbs, fixtures, and screens also produce the same colorless photons as the sun. Still even if the light looks natural, the mixture of photons is often quite different, and the light sources are only feet away from our eyes. The natural light spectrum is primarily healthy, but the electric light spectrum is often not so good for your health.

Color is in Your Head

If the light photons reaching us are colorless, how do we see colors? The magical transformation occurs in our visual system. Each colorless photon is color-coded when it interacts with the specific light-sensitive photopigments in our retina at

Sunlight shining on a crystal vase refracted into the visible spectrum of color wavelengths across a floor. (iStock/MiguelUrbelz)

the back of our eyes. Depending on its individual wavelength each photon triggers our perception of a specific color in the rainbow spectrum. Where a photon's wavelength lies in the visible range between 380 to 780 nanometers (nm = billionth of a meter) determines whether it is coded into violet, indigo, royal blue, sky blue, aqua/cyan, green, yellow, orange, or red. The highest energy visible photons have the shortest wavelengths (380-425 nm) and are perceived by the human brain as violet light. The lowest energy visible photons have the longest wavelengths (620-780 nm) and are seen as red.

We don't usually see the individual colors embedded in sunlight because the human brain perceives the almost even mix of the visible photon wavelengths in daylight as white light. It is only when that white light is split apart by a crystal, prism or by raindrops in the sky that we see the full rainbow-colored spectrum. In a rainbow, or the spectral colors displayed on a wall or floor, the visible photons from the sun are distributed in a continuous, seamless color display from 380 nm violet to 780 nm red.

When we design electric lighting, we want to achieve a color that resembles the white light from the sun, so that what we see in our surroundings looks natural. However, the white light provided by electric light is only a simulation of natural light. That is because it is possible to create something that looks like white light using different permutations and combinations of the various color wavelengths. Whenever the photons that generate different colors are correctly balanced, something resembling natural white light is created.

But this is harder to do than you might imagine. We don't all see the same colors, and even if we can see the same color, we may name it differently. Because color is a personal visual perception, defining the exact border between colors, such as blue and green or orange and red, is somewhat arbitrary.

This was vividly illustrated to me when we first tried to create white light that removed the harmful sky-blue photon wavelengths that disrupt circadian clocks at night. I thought we had something that looked very good, but when I showed it to a colleague, he told me it looked pinkish. I said, "You've got to be kidding, that's a beautiful white light". To prove my point, I brought in another couple of colleagues, but only one saw what I saw, and the other saw the light with a pink tint. We brought in more colleagues of different ages, racial origins, and gender and lo and behold, the opinions continued to be split 50:50. Clearly simulating white light was going to be more challenging than we had anticipated. Fortunately, we were eventually able to solve this problem, as we will discuss in Chapter 8: *Creating Healthy Light*.

Why Do People See Different Colors?

Some of the differences in color perception are cultural, as is explained so beautifully in Guy Deutscher's book, *Through the Language Glass*.[97] He tells how, in 1858, William Gladstone, a leading British politician and Greek scholar, was the first to recognize in his exhaustive analysis of Homer's Iliad and Odyssey that the ancient Greeks did not have a word for blue in their language. They undoubtedly saw what we call blue in the sky, and the waters of the Mediterranean Sea, but the normally precisely descriptive Greek language did not recognize blue as a distinct color. Another example is the traditional Japanese language that had one word, "ao", for blue and green, which is the reason that Japanese traffic lights use a blueish-green color. In contrast, the Russian language has two words for blue, and they can distinguish more adeptly than other cultures between light blue and dark blue colors.[98]

The number of colors that are described in the light spectrum is also somewhat arbitrary. Isaac Newton defined the rainbow spectrum as having seven colors - violet, indigo, blue, green, yellow, orange, and red. Because of the spiritual significance of the number seven, he chose to add indigo as a color between violet and blue.

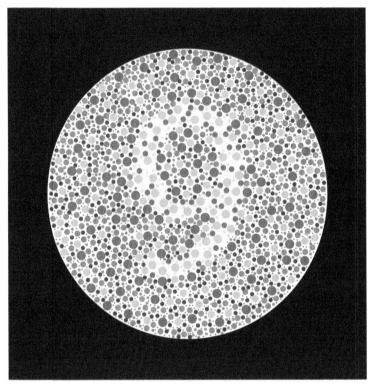

Example of color plate from the Ishihara color vision test. Some individuals cannot see the number 9 on this color plate. (iStock/Natallia Reshetova)

An individual's color perception also depends on the photopigments they have in their retina. Most people have three types of photopigments in their retinal cones. S-cones have an opsin photopigment with a peak sensitivity at ~420nm (violet), M-cones have an opsin with a peak sensitivity at ~534nm (green), and L-cones have an opsin with a peak sensitivity at ~564nm (yellow).[99] But 50% of women and about 8% of men have a fourth opsin photopigment, and therefore perceive a greater sense of color, and can see more distinct colors in the typical rainbow spectrum.[100]

A reduced sense of color is seen in the 8% of men and 0.5% of all women who have so-called "color blindness" defects in the photopigments in their cones. But color blindness is a misnomer. Most of these people have two photopigments instead of the usual three, and do see colors, but light photons falling on their eyes produce a different perception of color from the average person. And even among those with color vision defects, some may be perceiving different colors than others.

SCIENTIFIC ASIDE:
How to Test Your Color Vision

The most convenient way to determine if you have defects in your color vision is to take the test created by Professor Shinobu Ishihara at the University of Tokyo in 1917.[101] The Ishihara color plate test consists of a series of pictures comprised of multiple different color dots. Hidden within each plate is a number from 1 to 99. People with other color vision types see different numbers, or cannot see specific numbers, on the Ishihari plates. There are online versions available, but you need to be careful because if the color palate on the computer screen is distorted in any way it will give incorrect results.

Another cause of different perceptions of color is the yellowing of the lens in the eye as people age. It is a gradual effect, so a person doesn't recognize the changes until they undergo cataract surgery, where the lens is replaced with a new clear artificial lens. Suddenly, their perception of colors changes, often leading people after cataract surgery to want to redecorate their homes and change the paint colors on their walls.[102]

In the animal kingdom, the perception of color also depends on the photopigments.[103] Some, including frogs and marsupials, can see ultraviolet light that humans cannot see. Others, including some birds, have five different photopigments so they can see a much richer range of vibrant colors than we humans can enjoy. This raises considerable challenges for outdoor lighting which we will discuss in Chapter 12: *Light Pollution and Biodiversity*.

Describing colors, therefore, is very tricky, for you can never be sure that the other person is seeing what you see. Those who find themselves arguing with their spouse or partner about the choice of a color scheme, or whether the new sofa clashes with the carpet, can be reassured that both of you may be right!

What we can measure objectively is the spectral distribution and power of the different wavelengths of visible light using devices such as a spectrophotometer. So going forward we will talk about light photon wavelengths when we need to be precise about the human interactions with light. The chart below maps the wavelengths of photons from 300 to 800 nm against the colors of the light spectrum from invisible ultraviolet to invisible infrared. As we will discuss, photons at each of these different wavelengths have quite distinct specific interactions with the human body.

So that you can understand the full impact of the light to which you are exposed, let's take a quick tour across the light

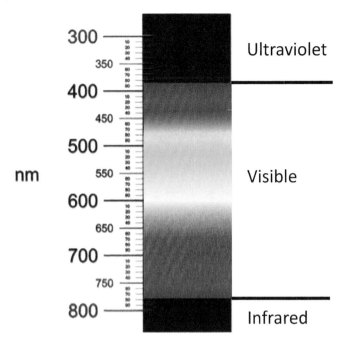

nm		
300		Ultraviolet
350		
400		
450		
500		
550		Visible
600		
650		
700		
750		
800		Infrared

The visible color and invisible ultraviolet and infrared wavelengths
of the optical window of the electromagnetic spectrum
(Adapted from iStock.com/leonarth)

spectrum from ultraviolet to infrared. As we do this, we will
have to debunk the misinformation, hype, and urban myths
that clutter the internet, and even some professional marketing
materials used in the eyewear and lighting industries.

Ultraviolet Light

Most of the ultraviolet photons that arrive from the sun are
absorbed by the Earth's atmosphere. The most damaging
high-energy UV photons with less than 200nm wavelength are
absorbed by oxygen molecules, and those between 200-300nm
are mostly absorbed by the ozone layer. Five percent of UV
that does penetrate to the surface of the Earth is 300 – 315
nm UV-B, and 95% is 315 – 400 nm UV-A. Only the highest

wavelength UV-A photons (380-400 nm range) are visible as a deep violet light, and the remaining UV-A and UV-B are invisible radiation.[104]

Outdoors, especially when the sun is high in the sky between 10 am and 2 pm, exposure to both UV-A and UV-B is highest. UV-B exposure can convert cholesterol in the skin to create Vitamin D, the hormone that strengthens our bones. Still the increased risk of skin cancer outweighs any positive benefits, so it is safer to get your Vitamin D3 from supplements.[105] UV-B penetrates less deeply into the skin, but because it has higher energy, it causes sunburn and can alter the DNA in your skin cells. UV-A is what gives you a suntan, and because it can penetrate more deeply it can cause your skin to age and wrinkle over time. Most sunscreen ointments, even with a high SP rating, block UV-B but not UV-A, and you need to ensure you choose a broad spectrum sunscreen to also protect against UV-A.[106]

UV-A, because it penetrates the lens of the eye, is primarily responsible for cataracts.[107] It is essential to make sure that your sunglasses provide complete protection against UV-A and UV-B. This protection is usually embedded in the lens, and has nothing to do with the darkness of the sunglasses, or whether they are polarized.[108]

Indoors, there is no UV-B, as it cannot penetrate through windows, and the intensity of UV-A from daylight drops rapidly with distance from the window. Light fixtures do provide limited amounts of UV-A, but the levels are thousands of times lower than sunlight outside. Interestingly, the small amount of UV-A in some LED lights interacts with the optical brighteners in fabrics and other materials to make the colors pop, or seem "whiter than white" in store displays lit with these lights.

High Energy Visible (HEV) Light

The term High Energy Visible, or HEV light is used to describe the photons in the blue-violet end of the visible light spectrum (between 380-500 nm, which have shorter wavelengths and higher energy than the photons we perceive as green, yellow, orange and red.

Blatant misinformation and irresponsible marketing hype occurs when all HEV light is referred to as "blue" or as a "blue hazard" to alarm people so they will buy blue-blocking glasses, or get blue-blocking artificial lenses installed in their eyes. In reality, the various parts of the violet-blue spectrum have very different health effects, some of which are positive and others that may sometimes be negative. So, beware of loose claims and statements that lump all blue wavelengths together.

Furthermore, any claimed hazards of certain specific blue wavelengths are highly dependent on light intensity, and whether you are outdoors or indoors. To clarify the impact of so-called HEV light, we will look at each separate part of the violet-blue color range.

Violet Light

As we have discussed, there is no sharp boundary between each perceived color of light, but for this discussion, we will define violet light as wavelengths between 400 and 425 nm. While all blue wavelengths are stimulating and alerting, violet light in the 415-425 nm range is the most alerting and effective at combating drowsiness.[109]

Violet light also has antibacterial properties. Peak effectiveness at killing bacteria such as staphylococcus occurs at 405nm.[110] So, illuminating the surfaces in a room with 405 nm light can provide a viable disinfectant, but only if the surface is directly exposed to the light.

Indigo Light

Indigo is a blueish-violet color that has a wavelength range between about 425 and 450 nm. In bright outdoor sunlight, especially in the middle of the day, indigo-blue photons can cause apoptosis, which means cell death in the retina of the eye.[111] But this risk only occurs when we are exposed to bright sunlight, or if you are using a welding arc lamp.[112]

This outdoor "blue light hazard" can be minimized by using eyewear that filters out this light. Dark sunglasses, or welder's goggles, can prevent 50% or more of the light from reaching the eye. Certain types of blue-reflecting eyewear, for example,

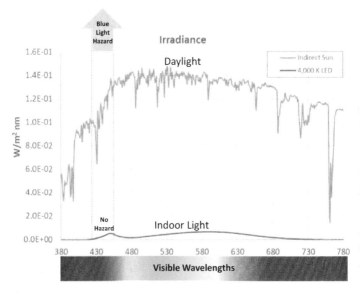

The so-called "Blue Light Hazard" from 425-450nm blue wavelengths is never an issue indoors even in a brightly lit room at 400 lux light intensity, the blue irradiance indoors is so much lower than the blue delivered by 10,000 lux daylight outside. The Blue Light Hazard only becomes an issue in bright 50,000 - 100,000 lux sunlight which is 5-10 times brighter than the indirect daylight level shown in this chart.
(Adapted from Bretschneider E (2018) with permission.
Archived at https://perma.cc/5L3F-2FKD)

Eyezen+ lenses, selectively block at least 20% of the high energy wavelengths found in 425-450 nm indigo-blue light.[113]

Indoors, despite all the marketing hype, there is no 425-450 nm blue light hazard because light intensity levels are 100 - 1,000 times less than they are outdoors on a sunny day.[114] No lamp, computer screen, or cell phone can generate levels of indigo-blue light bright enough to cause any retinal damage, macular degeneration, or cataracts.

As I write these words, I am sitting with my eyes about 20 inches away from a sizeable 32-inch computer screen. But only 100 lux of light is entering my eyes compared to the 100,000 lux of light to which I would be exposed if I took a walk on a beach on a sunny day. Therefore, there is no way that my computer screen is delivering enough indigo-blue light to damage my eyes.

Because there have been so many exaggerations and false claims from vendors selling eyewear, intraocular lenses, and screens, various international scientific and professional bodies have had to make clarifying statements. For example, the CIE International Commission on Illumination in 2019 issued the statement that: "The blue light hazard is not an issue for white-light sources used in general lighting. Claims that exposure to blue light may be linked to the risk of age-related macular degeneration ... are not supported by the peer-reviewed literature."[115] Furthermore, they stated, "the term "blue light hazard" should not be used when referring to circadian rhythm disruption or sleep disturbance", as we will discuss in the next section.

Do all these claims and counterclaims leave you confused? How can you know whether the blue-blocking glasses you are being offered by your optician, or on an eyewear website are really necessary or helpful? This will become much clearer when I discuss eyewear solutions in Chapter 11: *When You Don't Control the Space*, but for now be cautious when someone uses the term "blue light hazard".

Royal Blue – Sky Blue Light

At longer blue wavelengths, between 450 nm to 495 nm, the color we see transitions into the royal blue to sky-blue color palate. Photons in this range have biologically important effects that are critical for our health but occur so automatically that we are unaware of them. During the daytime hours, blue light photons in the 460-495 nm range are the most potent in synchronizing our circadian clocks and strengthening our circadian rhythms which are so important for health. But during the nocturnal hours, between sunset and sunrise, when our circadian system is most sensitive, blue light in a broader range between 440 and 495 nm can cause circadian disruption and precipitate the host of medical disorders we have discussed in previous chapters.[116]

The effects of blue light are not confined to the eyes. Compared to ultraviolet and violet photons, blue photons penetrate more deeply into the skin, and the depth increases with increasing wavelength.[117] The blue photons only penetrate a few millimeters, but that makes all the difference in treating newborn babies who have become jaundiced. Their immature livers cannot clear the blood of a yellow-orange pigment called bilirubin that is made when red blood cells break down. It is a serious problem because if bilirubin levels get too high in the baby's blood, it can impair brain development, resulting in learning disabilities and may cause death.

Judy Ward, an observant nurse in charge of the premature unit at Rochdale Hospital in Essex, England, discovered the curative effect of light.[118] She believed that fresh air and sunlight were good for newborn babies, so she sneaked them outside on sunny days. But then she noticed in the summer of 1956 that in a baby who was jaundiced, the sunlight caused the yellow skin color to disappear except for where a diaper covered it. The pediatrician in charge, Dr Richard Cremer, tried various lights and was able to replicate the effect by using blue light. Subsequent research showed the peak effect occurs at 460 nm. Jaundice is reversed very effectively in these babies when they are placed naked (except for a diaper) in a lightbox beaming blue light. Light in the range of 460-490 nm is effective as the longer wavelengths penetrate deeper, which compensates for the reduced effectiveness in destroying bilirubin.[119]

Green Light

Our color vision system is most sensitive to green light at 555 nm. This means that if energy efficiency is your top goal in lighting, then you can get the greatest perceived brightness of visible light for a given amount of electrical energy using 555 nm photons.

The perceived brightness of visible light emitted by a light bulb or fixture is measured in lumens, and the amount of electricity used to create that light is measured in watts. Hence, lumens per watt is a measure of the efficiency of turning electrical energy into perceptually bright light. You can get white light from a traditional incandescent light bulb at 15 lumens per watt, and from a typical LED light at about 100 lumens per watt. At the eco-conscious Hotel Gat near Checkpoint Charlie in Berlin, Germany, you can stay in a room lit with pure green light at an energy efficiency potentially close to 683 lumens per watt.[120] This may have appeal as a novelty value, but most of us would rather live under light that is whiter in color. That trade-off can only be achieved by mixing green light with other less electrically efficient colors. As a result, you cannot get white light with

A room at the Hotel Gat Point Charlie in Berlin, Germany lit by monochromatic green light near the 555nm peak of luminous efficiency. (Courtesy Hotel Gat Point Charlie, Berlin)

an electrical efficiency greater than 100-200 lumens per watt.

As I will discuss in future chapters, lumens per watt predominantly measures the electrical efficiency of producing green and yellow photons. It does not reflect the blue and red content of light which are essential for health. High lumens per watt light can be very unhealthy and the single-minded focus on regulating light according to the measured lumens per watt has serious adverse effects on human health.

Green light photons at 525 nm also appear to be effective in reducing pain in patients with severe chronic migraines and those with fibromyalgia.[121] By seating people in front of green lights, or providing green light goggles, significant reductions in the frequency of migraines and other chronic pain have been reported in animal studies and human patients by researchers at the Department of Anesthesiology at Duke University and the University of Arizona Chronic Pain Center.[122]

Yellow - Orange Light

Light in the yellow to orange range is what predominates when violet, blue, and green light is significantly reduced or absent. There are three main reasons why this is done.

Sodium vapor lights were first introduced in the 1930s because they were more energy efficient at producing visible bright light (initially 40 but now approaching 200 lumens per watt) and longer lasting than incandescent or other lights.[123] They are primarily used in streetlights, or as outdoor lights in industrial facilities, because they emit a strong yellow color peaking at 589 nm, which makes distinguishing between different color objects difficult. In the 1960's high pressure sodium vapor lamps were introduced, which have a somewhat broader spectrum but are still predominantly yellow.

Semiconductor factories have yellow clean rooms, where all high-energy visible light is removed. This is critical because the process of photolithography in which the integrated circuits are etched onto the semiconductor chips is very sensitive to any UV, violet or blue light photons under 500 nm.[124]

Finally, certain types of circadian-friendly lighting for night applications have a yellow-orange color because all blue wavelengths are eliminated or filtered out.[125] As we will discuss, this is not the only solution to prevent circadian disruption by light at night, but it is a validated method.

The challenge with using yellow or yellow-orange light is that it has much lower alerting effects than light that contains blue or violet – the most stimulatory wavelengths.[126] Hence it is harder to stay awake and alert at night under yellow-orange light, especially if you are sleep deprived.

Red Light

Red light photons can penetrate skin more deeply than lower wavelength photons and impact cellular processes. The best-studied application is the use of 650 nm red light to stimulate hair growth in people with thinning hair.[127] The hair follicles that generate the hair go through three phases – growth (anagen) degeneration (catagen) and rest (telogen). Red light promotes the growth phase and inhibits the degeneration phase, and can produce a measurably increased rate of hair growth.

Red light at 670 nm stimulates mitochondria in the retina and can improve vision in older people.[128] Other applications of red light include accelerating wound healing after surgery and radiation.[129]

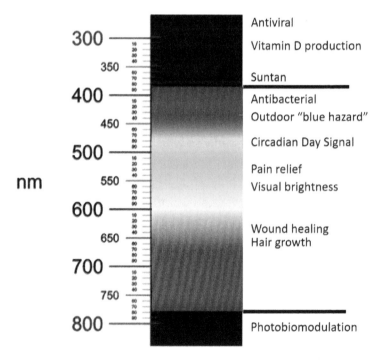

Each color wavelength in the full spectrum of sunlight has specific health effects which may not be provided by the much dimmer and more limited spectra of electric lights. (Adapted from iStock.com/leonarth)

Infrared Light

Infrared photons can penetrate much more deeply than red or other visible photons, and can penetrate the human skull and reach the brain. This has opened up a set of treatments using photobiomodulation that provide infrared light in rhythmic patterns that mimic theta or gamma frequencies, the predominant brain waves in healthy people.[130]

Indoor Lighting is a Choice

By now, you will have realized that there are a wide variety of distinct effects of the different photon wavelengths that reach us as visible light. All of them depend on the intensity of the light at a given wavelength – referred to as "photon flux", which is the number of photons hitting us per second. When you are outside in direct sunlight, you are exposed to a high photon flux at each wavelength across the full spectrum of visible light from violet to red. There is enough sky-blue light to synchronize your circadian clocks, enough violet and blue to keep you awake and alert, enough green to see in vivid color vision, and maybe enough red to grow your hair!

But indoors, under electric light, the overall intensity or photon flux of visible light is 1,000 times less. You just cannot achieve all the benefits of sunlight, even if you provide full spectrum light, and so you are forced to make choices and tradeoffs. Synchronizing your circadian clocks with enough sky-blue light photons during the day and removing these sky-blue photons at night is a priority that has direct benefits for your health. So is good visual acuity, so you can clearly see your surroundings, and can work and play effectively and safely indoors. But other goals of indoor lighting often have to take second priority.

We will address the design of healthy and effective spectrally-engineered lighting in the next section of this book.

In this chapter, you have learned:

1. Light is composed of colorless photons that trigger visual color and non-visual responses in the retina, depending on their energy and wavelength.

2. Sunlight typically provides 1,000 times more photons across the full range of spectral colors than indoor light, and there is no evidence of any blue hazard to your eyes when you are indoors.

3. Because indoor light is much less intense, we have to make careful choices of the spectral colors in our light sources to ensure they enhance and protect our health.

5
─────

You Have the Right to Healthy Light

There are no valid excuses for delaying the transition to healthy circadian lights.

Take a walk down the lighting aisles of your local hardware store, and you will find an overwhelming diversity of lamps and fixtures. But almost all light bulbs that you can buy today for your home are blue-chip LED products. Gone are the incandescent, halogen and fluorescent lights of the past. We have entered the era of the blue pump LED.

It is the same story when you peruse the catalogs and websites of the commercial lighting manufacturers who supply offices, schools, hospitals, senior living, retail, and everywhere else. The blue-chip LED reigns supreme.

Despite more than 20 years of scientific evidence showing that blue-rich light in the evening disrupts our circadian clocks, sleep, and health, we have created a world where virtually the

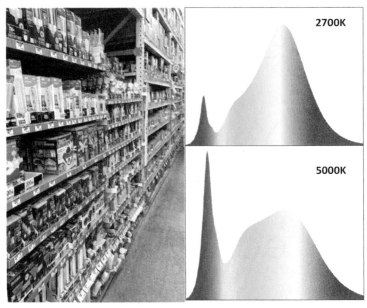

Most of the lights you can buy in the hardware store are now blue-chip LEDs of different color temperatures, but all with a spike of blue light that can be harmful in the evenings and at night.
(Copyright Circadian Light Research Center)

only illumination you can buy is unchanging blue-rich light. And this LED light typically delivers too little blue for daytime health, and far too much blue for the evening hours.

There are exceptions. In Chapter 10: *How to be a Smart Consumer,* and Chapter 11: *When You Don't Control the Space,* I will show you how to find lights to provide the lighting you need to promote and protect circadian health. However, circadian lighting is still a tiny fraction of the lighting market.

A recent market research survey estimated the global circadian lighting market at $261 million, compared to the total worldwide lighting market of ~$150 Billion per year.[131] This represents only a 0.2% market share, which is an overestimate because they used an overly generous interpretation of what constitutes circadian lighting. For example, they counted white color-tuning as "circadian lighting" where high color temperature light is provided during the day and low color temperature light in the evening. As we will discuss in Chapter 8: *Creating Healthy Light* merely changing the color or coordinated color temperature (CCT) of light often doesn't provide effective circadian light.

Why Do So Few Lights Support Circadian Health?

When lighting manufacturers, lighting designers, and salespeople are asked why fewer than 0.2% of the lights sold today have any circadian or healthy features, they typically have three answers.

1. **Lack of Consumer Demand**

    First, the lighting industry will tell you their customers are not asking for circadian lights.

    > *"You ask whose idea it was to use blue LEDs to light the world at night? The answer is the consumer. There have been so many innovations over the years in LED lighting where we thought we were providing a new benefit that would drive sales and give our products market differentiation. If it didn't lower the cost of the device for the consumer, it didn't get traction. If the modifications can be made with little or no cost impact for the consumer, it has a chance. Stand in the aisle at Home Depot and ask someone buying light bulbs what the Lighting Facts label tells them and how it informs their purchasing decision. I'll bring the bucket of ice cold water to pour on you :)"*
    > **Lighting product developer**.

    This is true because the only features that consumers have

been taught to look for when choosing lights are 1) cost, 2) color, and 3) energy efficiency (in order of priority). Most people are quite unaware of the adverse health impacts of the wrong light at the wrong time.

This is why I have written *THE LIGHT DOCTOR* to create widespread awareness of the electric health havoc that modern lighting is creating, and to explain why you must demand healthy circadian lights to safeguard your and your family's health.

2. Single-Minded Focus on Energy Efficiency

Second, the lighting industry will tell you that new energy regulations force them to focus on energy efficiency rather than healthy lighting.

> *"The Biden-Harris Administration, through the U.S. Department of Energy (DOE), today proposed stronger efficiency standards for light bulbs, also known as general service lamps, to conserve energy and cut energy bills for American families and consumers ... (This) represents a key pillar of the President's strategy to tackle the climate crisis while lowering costs for families.... Today's proposed rule significantly raises the minimum lightbulb efficiency level, from 45 to over 120 lumens per watt for the most common bulbs."* **Press release US Department of Energy December 19, 2022.**[132]

To comply with the high lumens per watt light bulb regulations of the US Department of Energy, manufacturers must use blue-chip LEDs. A similar 120 lumens per watt standard is planned by the European Union.[133] In the United Kingdom, the proposed minimum energy performance for lighting is the highest in the world, at 120 lumens per watt beginning in September 2023 and climbing to 140 lumens per watt in 2027.[134] These standards are currently not possible to achieve with spectrally-engineered lights that regulate blue emissions across day and night to provide circadian health and performance.

We all have a right to healthy light indoors and outdoors
that strengthens our circadian rhythms and protects our health.
(Adapted from (iStock.com/Wavebreakmedia)

Why are the regulators forcing a future of harsh blue-rich LED lights upon us? It is because they have adopted flawed metrics such as lumens per watt, which measure the perceptual brightness of light and not its healthiness. They justify the regulations based on the reduction of greenhouse gases, and reduction of pollution but fail to recognize the much larger immediate human health costs and impact on the natural environment of expanding the use of blue-rich light at night.

Cleary we need to do a much better job of educating our politicians and regulators. You and I have a right to healthy light! The climate lobby has been very effective at communicating its message. We need to do a better job of communicating ours.

3. Science is Not Ready

Third, the lighting industry has claimed that the science of circadian lighting has yet to be proven, or is contradictory. This is partly an excuse by the industry to procrastinate on circadian lighting, and partly a failure of the scientific community to communicate how well-established is the core science of circadian clocks and light.

"Scientists only speak to each other, and not to their neighbors."
(iStock.com/undefined)

> *"The reason ... circadian lighting is not penetrating in the market is that nobody knows about it. Scientists know, but they only talk to each other. If you talk to your neighbor, they won't know."* **Jan Denneman, chairman of Good Light Group, an Eindhoven, Holland–based nonprofit advocating healthy lighting.**[135]

In Chapter 4: *Human Light Interaction*, I carefully distinguished between validated science, misinformation, and marketing hype regarding the so-called "blue light hazard". So, how can I prove that what I say in this book is based on rigorous scientific evidence? Am I the lone advocate of my own opinions on lighting, or am I reporting on the consensus opinion of the leading scientists in the field of circadian rhythms, light, and health?

These are fair questions, so I addressed them by seeking the help of 248 of the world's leading scientists in this field. Together, we identified a series of statements that summarize what the science of circadian rhythms and light has firmly established so far.

SCIENTIFIC ASIDE:
How We Established a Scientific Consensus

First, I recruited the help of three leading scientists to create a list of potential scientific statements. Professor David Blask of Tulane University has done pioneering research on the carcinogenic effects of light on breast cancer and prostate cancer. Professor Sean Cain of Monash University in Australia has done significant research on the impact of light on people living their regular lives. Professor Randy Nelson of the Rockefeller Neuroscience Institute at West Virginia University has shown how exposure to light at night increases body mass gain and depressive-like responses, as well as impairs cognition, immune function, and recovery from cardiac arrest and stroke.

Together we composed a set of 40 statements laying out some of the core conclusions that could be potentially made from the 30,000 peer-reviewed scientific articles published on the science of light and circadian rhythms. To avoid the bias of only picking scientists who agreed with our opinions, we invited every scientist in the world who had published more than four peer-reviewed scientific papers on circadian rhythms and light since 2008 to assess

the 40 statements. Using the comprehensive PubMed database of scientific articles to search for all papers with the terms "circadian" + "light", we googled every scientific author with four or more publications to collect their email addresses from their university or publications websites.

Two hundred forty-eight leading scientists from around the world, all of whom are experts on the effects of light on circadian rhythms, responded to our invitation to evaluate each of the 40 statements. For each statement they indicated whether there was no evidence, limited evidence, or good scientific evidence to support it, or that the statement was scientifically well established. When the results were compiled, we found the scientists had reached a consensus on the following 25 statements firmly based on scientific evidence. The complete research results have been published in a peer-reviewed scientific journal.[136]

Scientific Consensus on Circadian Lighting

Consensus was reached on the following 25 statements among the 248 leading scientists, who had between them published 2,697 peer-reviewed scientific publications on circadian clocks and light since 2008. Publishing an article in a peer-reviewed journal is a high scientific standard which is not easily achieved as it means other scientists have critically examined and accepted the research findings and conclusions.

1. **Robust circadian rhythms are important for maintaining good health.**

Circadian rhythms are most robust when they are tightly synchronized to the natural day-night cycle, and the circadian clocks throughout the body are tightly synchronized with each other. Circadian rhythms under these conditions typically show the greatest amplitude (widest swing between daily maximum and minimum levels). When circadian rhythms are robust, sleep during the night is most restorative, mood, alertness and cognitive performance during the day are enhanced, and the immune system's capability to ward off disease is strongest.

2. **Disrupting circadian rhythms can cause ill-health.**

There is a broad scientific consensus that disrupting the human circadian clock system precipitates a wide range of medical disorders as I discussed in Chapters 1: *Edison's Cancer Epidemic* and 2: *Goodbye Milky Way*. Circadian disruption can have many different types of significant adverse health effects in children, young adults and in the elderly. These include obesity, diabetes, heart disease and breast cancer.

3. **Regular daily exposure to daylight enhances circadian entrainment and strengthens circadian rhythms.**

Getting outside at a *regular time each day*, especially in the mornings, and being exposed to natural daylight, is well established as an effective way to keep our circadian rhythms firmly synchronized. In the absence of regular exposure to daylight, our circadian rhythms can become dissociated and flattened and ill-health and susceptibility to disease can result. Regular exposure to daylight strengthens our circadian rhythms and tightens their entrainment by the natural cycle of day and night.

4. **Regular daily exposure to daylight can enhance sleep at night.**

As we discussed in Chapter 2: *Goodbye Milky Way*, the average person spends over 90% of their time indoors under twilight levels of lighting. The lack of a strong contrast in light exposure between day and night is a major contributor to the sleep problems that are so common today. Regular daily exposure to outdoor sunlight, or even cloudy overcast daylight, helps deepen and extend our uninterrupted nocturnal sleep.

5. **Increasing indoor light intensity during daytime can enhance circadian entrainment and strengthen circadian rhythms.**

Since we tend to live indoors in twilight levels of light, our circadian rhythms can become dampened and lose their tight associations with natural day and night. Increasing the brightness of indoor light during daytime hours, especially if it is rich in blue wavelengths, helps to compensate by synchronizing our circadian rhythms to the natural day-night cycle – a process called entrainment. At the same time the entrained circadian rhythms show an increased amplitude – a greater contrast between peak and trough of the daily rhythm.

6. **Increasing indoor light intensity during daytime can improve daytime alertness and reduce sleepiness.**

Natural light from offices with windows, and bright electric light indoors, especially when it has significant blue content, has an alerting effect, and reduces sleepiness. This combats the natural tendency to drowsiness when we live under twilight conditions.

7. **Increasing indoor light intensity at night increases the disruption of circadian rhythms.**

Our eyes and brain are highly sensitive to light during the nighttime hours (from sunset to sunrise), and the disruptive effects on our circadian rhythms get more pronounced the brighter the light intensity. This effect is exacerbated by lights with high blue content such as LEDs or fluorescent lights.

8. **Increasing indoor light intensity at night increases the suppression of nocturnal melatonin production.**

Melatonin is the pineal hormone that plays an important role in signaling the darkness of night to all the cells of the body and their internal circadian clocks. When we live outdoors in the natural world, as we discussed with the Rocky Mountain campers in Chapter 2: *Goodbye Milky Way*, melatonin rises at sunset and falls at dawn. But when we use electric lights, we suppress the melatonin signal and may shift it. Our internal circadian clocks interpret electric light at night as a shift in the timing of day and night. The brighter the electric light at night the more suppressed and shifted is the melatonin rhythm.

9. **Repetitive and prolonged exposure to light at night bright enough to cause circadian disruption increases the risk of breast cancer in women.**

As we discussed in Chapter 1: *Edison's Cancer Epidemic*, the first reports were published in 2000 showing a significantly increased risk of breast cancer in women exposed to light on the night shift. Since then, several national and international scientific bodies have reviewed the considerable accumulated evidence from hundreds of human epidemiological and animal model studies. After reviewing all the evidence, the WHO International Agency for Research on Cancer, and the National

Toxicology Program of US National Institutes of Health have linked light exposure at night to circadian disruption and to the significant increase in the rate of new breast cancer cases.

10. **Repetitive and prolonged exposure to light at night bright enough to cause circadian disruption increases the risk of obesity and diabetes.**

A substantial body of evidence has accumulated in recent years showing up to twice the risk of obesity and diabetes in people who are exposed to light at night, either by leaving the lights on in the bedroom at night, or by working on night shifts. As we discussed in Chapter 2: *Goodbye Milky Way*, these effects can start developing even after only one night of light exposure.

11. **Repetitive and prolonged exposure to light at night bright enough to cause circadian disruption increases the risk of sleep disorders.**

Light at night has three key effects on sleep. First it alerts and stimulates our brain which makes it harder to fall asleep or stay asleep. Second it shifts our circadian clocks so the timing of when we can easily fall asleep is shifted. Third it disrupts our circadian clocks and the architecture of the various sleep stages such as REM and non-REM sleep, so that sleep is disrupted and not as fully restorative.

12. **The sensitivity peak of the ipRGC melanopic receptors in the human retina is approximately 480nm in the blue part of the visible spectrum.**

As we discussed in Chapter 3: *Clockwork Blue*, a major breakthrough in circadian science was the discovery of the intrinsically photosensitive retinal ganglion cell (ipRGC) receptors in the eye that detect the blue wavelengths in light.

The peak sensitivity of these ipRGC receptors is to sky-blue light at about 480 nm.

13. **The most potent wavelengths for circadian entrainment are 460-495 nm blue light near to the sensitivity peak of the ipRGC melanopic receptors.**

While the ipRGC receptors have their peak sensitivity at about 480 nm, they can sense a broader range of blue light photons. Blue light is most potent in synchronizing human circadian clocks to the environmental day-night cycle, a process called "entrainment", in the 460-495 nm range near the 480 nm peak sensitivity.

Blue-enriched (460-495nm) light in the evening (during the three hours before bedtime) ...

14. disrupts nocturnal sleep more than blue-depleted light at the same intensity

15. phase delays the circadian system more than blue-depleted light at the same intensity.

16. disrupts circadian rhythms more than blue-depleted light at the same intensity.

When you are exposed to light containing potent 460-495 nm blue wavelengths in the evening after sunset, it shifts and disrupts your circadian rhythms and impairs your sleep at night. As we will discuss in Chapter 8: *Creating Healthy Light* we are sensitive to an even broader range of 440-495nm blue during overnight hours. The solution is to use blue-depleted light at night – i.e. light without those disruptive blue wavelengths – rather than conventional LED lights which are rich in blue. This greatly reduces the risk of shifting our circadian clocks, and disrupting our sleep.

17. **Exposure to 460-495nm blue light at night suppresses melatonin production.**

Because we are so sensitive to blue light at night, a broad range of blue wavelengths can suppress pineal melatonin production. The strongest suppression occurs with blue light wavelengths between 460 and 495 nm. These blue wavelengths interfere with the signaling of natural darkness by melatonin and undermine the important protective effects of melatonin at night, such as suppressing cancer cells in the body, as we discussed in Chapter 1: *Edison's Cancer Epidemic.*

18. **Exposure to 460-495nm blue light at night disrupts circadian rhythms.**

These same 460 - 495 nm blue wavelengths during the nighttime hours have the largest effect in disrupting circadian rhythms. These blue wavelengths are 25 times more potent than full spectrum white light which contains all the wavelength of the visible light spectrum. Exposure to even a small amount of blue light at night is highly disruptive to circadian rhythms.

Practical Applications

The 248 scientific experts were then asked about the practical implications of the well-established science of circadian-light interactions and reached a consensus on the following statements:

19. **Light used in the evening (during the three hours before bedtime) should have as little blue content as practically possible.**

We become increasingly sensitive to the blue content in our electric lights as the evening progresses. Thus, it is important to replace your lights in the places you spend your evenings, such as the family room, bathroom and bedroom, with lights that have very little or no blue content. We will discuss how to do that in later chapters of THE LIGHT DOCTOR.

20. **The risk of circadian disruption during the three hours before bedtime can be reduced either by 1) dimming indoor lighting which may compromise the ability to perform visual work tasks, or 2) reducing the blue content of indoor lighting maintained at the intensity required for visual tasks.**

There are two ways of addressing the problem with blue-rich light during the evening hours. Since what matters is the total number of blue photons that you are exposed to per second, you can dim your existing conventional lights significantly to reduce the total amount of light to which you are exposed. The problem is that this may make it hard to read, or difficult for your children to do their homework. Alternatively, you can replace your current lights with low blue content lights so you can maintain illumination at your preferred levels.

21. **The blue content of light entering the eyes is much more important in determining circadian health outcomes than the correlated color temperature (CCT) of the light source.**

Changing the color of lights, measured as correlated color temperature or "CCT", has been touted by the lighting industry as a way to reduce blue content. Unfortunately, this is a highly misleading marketing strategy which does very little to address the problem. At the key 460 - 495 sky-blue wavelengths high CCT and low CCT electric lights can have very little difference in blue content, as they are all based on blue-pump LEDs. It is far more important to know the blue content of the lights that you are using than their CCT or color appearance.

22. **Increasing the energy efficiency of lights is desirable, but not if it increases the risks of causing circadian disruption and serious illness.**

Since the widespread introduction of LED lights in 2013, the lighting industry has been focused on promoting and improving the energy efficiency of LEDs. It has been the key selling proposition which has enabled blue-enriched LEDs to dominate the lighting market. While maximizing energy efficiency is, of course, desirable, failing to address the adverse health impact of energy-efficient blue-enriched LEDs is a much more significant problem. These blue-rich LEDs can increase your exposure to blue light at night, and accelerate the electric circadian havoc and ill-health caused by electric light.

23. **LED lights with high 460 - 495nm blue content should carry the warning label "maybe harmful if used at night"**

There was strong consensus among the 248 leading scientists researching the impact of light on circadian rhythms, that the evidence is now clear than blue-enriched LED lights with high 460 - 495 nm blue light content should carry a hazard warning label related to their use at night. This is justified by the increased risk of obesity, diabetes, heart disease and several types of cancer that are associated with exposure to excessive blue wavelengths at night.

24. **There is now sufficient evidence to support the widespread introduction of circadian lighting that adjusts light intensity and blue content across day and night to maintain robust circadian entrainment and health.**

There was also strong consensus that the lighting industry needs to transition to circadian lighting where the brightness of light and its blue content are varied by time of day. During the daytime hours indoor lights should be rich in sky-blue wavelengths, and during the nighttime hours from sunset to sunrise these sky-blue wavelengths should be removed.

25. **There is significant variation in individual sensitivity to light, therefore circadian lighting should be optimized where possible using personalized solutions.**

Some people are much more sensitive to the blue content of light than others, and it is important to adjust the blue content in electric lighting to make allowance for these more sensitive people. Furthermore, the orientation of our circadian clocks in relation to day and night may differ somewhat between individuals. Some of us are early rising "larks" and then fall asleep earlier in the evening. Others are genetically more sensitive to blue rich light in the evening and their sleep patterns may be delayed. As we discussed in Chapter 2: *Goodbye Milky Way*, these differences between people are reduced by regular exposure to natural outdoor light during the day.

You Have the Right to Healthy Light

As lighting consumers, you should demand the right to have healthy lights in your homes, workplaces, schools, hospitals, and everywhere else you frequent.

We can dismiss the claims by the lighting industry that the science is not ready. Our survey of the 248 leading scientists debunks these claims and provides an urgency to implement healthy lighting.

In the following chapters I will show that we can create and validate circadian lighting which provides health and well-being which is our right.

In this chapter, you have learned:

1. The lighting industry justifies its failure to provide circadian lighting that varies brightness and blue content by time of day because a) customers are not asking for circadian lights and b) by falsely claiming the science is not yet proven or is contradictory.

2. A survey of 248 of the world's leading scientists researching the impact of light on circadian rhythms and health, confirms that the science explained in THE LIGHT DOCTOR is well-validated, and that there is an urgent need to replace harmful blue-rich LEDs at night with healthy circadian lighting.

3. You have the right to healthy light and should campaign for it everywhere you spend your time indoors.

PART 2:

ENGINEERING

THE SOLUTION

6

Bringing the Outside Indoors

The challenges of illuminating our buildings with natural daylight. It used to be the only option, but we got lazy with the invention of electric light.

The indiscriminate use of electric light has got us in trouble, and now we need to be creative in finding solutions to the health crises we have created. The global lighting industry has grown into a ~$150 billion-a-year behemoth by focusing almost solely on illumination aesthetics and energy efficiency at the lowest cost.[137] As I will discuss in the following chapters of THE LIGHT DOCTOR, effective healthy lighting solutions are now available. Still, it will take consumer insistence – this means you – and maybe regulatory warning labels, to turn this massive lighting industry around.

In the old days, before electric light was conceived, our ancestors spent much more of their time outdoors exposed to the health-giving rays of the sun, and when they were indoors, their architecture was designed to let in natural blue-rich daylight. Then

Before electric light, most people spent their days outside exposed to blue-rich daylight. (Les Très Riches Heures du duc de Berry, folio 9)

after the sun had set, fires and candles emitting virtually no blue light were used to extend the wakeful day before they retired to sleep. These were the conditions that were recreated in the Rocky Mountain camping trips that we discussed in Chapter 2: *Goodbye Milky Way*, where the campers' circadian rhythms and sleep patterns became robust and healthy under the high-blue day, low-blue night, lighting conditions of the pre-electric natural world.[138]

Fundamentally, there are three solutions for ensuring circadian health:

1. Spend more time outside – especially in the mornings at a regular time

2. Bring daylight indoors – which has its limitations, as we will discuss in the chapter, and

3. Redesign electric light to provide blue-rich days and blue-free nights - which is addressed in the next three chapters.

How Much Time Should We Spend Outside?

Outdoor exposure to natural daylight provides the greatest boost to our health. People who spend sufficient time outside each day, sleep better and longer at night, and are healthier. They also live longer. Most important is the exposure to bright blue-rich daylight in the morning hours before the sun is high in the sky. This is when daylight is most effective at synchronizing our internal clocks and preventing the drifting apart of our circadian rhythms.

 SCIENTIFIC ASIDE: What is Daylight?

Daylight is a dynamic and complex mixture of direct sunlight, scattered light from the sky, and reflected light from nearby vegetation and buildings.

Scattering occurs when tiny particles and molecules in our atmosphere preferentially absorb and then scatter blue light photons in the Rayleigh effect, accounting for the blue skies on a sunny day, as discussed in Chapter 3: *Clockwork Blue*. In contrast, all the visible wavelengths of sunlight entering clouds are equally scattered in all directions by water droplets larger than 20 micrometers in size (called Mie scattering) so that the clouds emit full spectrum light and, therefore, appear white.[139] The underside of clouds appears dark only when they are too deep, or too dense with water droplets, to let sunlight through.

Much of the light that reaches the Earth, either as direct sunlight or scattered light from the sky, is reflected off trees, other vegetation, buildings, and other objects in our landscape before it reaches us. The colors we see depend on which light wavelength photons are absorbed by the object and which are reflected. So, because the leaves of plants and trees contain chloroplasts, they absorb blue and orange-red light to photosynthesize sugar nutrients, but reflect the green photons. This is why the leaves appear green, and the reflected light from vegetation is relatively richer in green wavelengths.

Daylight is dynamic because the sun is constantly moving across the sky, or more accurately our sky is moving across our sun. As it moves, this alters the amount, direction and type of light scattering and light reflection. Add to that ever-changing weather conditions. The result is a dynamic daylight experience that our ever-constant electric light does not replicate.

Today, less than 2% of the population of the developed world works outdoors. Unless you are a farmer, forester, or landscape gardener, finding the time to spend outdoors takes effort. Before the Industrial Revolution, and in the underdeveloped world today, 70-80% of the population worked on the land. Given that most of us don't want to return to that outdoor life, what is the minimum amount of daylight we need?

A study of 593 people working at home during the COVID-19 pandemic showed significant benefits when people spent 1-2 hours outside in natural daylight each day. Thirty minutes was not enough, but once they spent 60 minutes or more outside, sleep quality and alertness were improved, and anxiety and depression were reduced.[140]

Other studies have shown a reduction in body weight in people exposed to natural outdoor light. Body fat levels are reduced by exposure to bright daylight in the mornings.[141] This speaks to the fundamental effects on our metabolism when our circadian clocks are correctly aligned and our circadian rhythms made more robust.

Ideally, you would get outside and expose yourself to daylight within an hour after dawn or an hour after waking, whichever comes later. This timing provides the maximum light resetting signal to the circadian clock but avoids truncating your sleep and making you unnecessarily sleep-deprived. As you find light having its beneficial effects, the morning light exposure may gradually move your waking time earlier.

But life is complex, and the demands on your time are many, so your outdoor light exposure should be every morning, as early as is practical.

Bringing Daylight Inside

If you cannot get outside because of inclement weather, conflicting commitments, or infirmity, the second-best option is to bring the daylight inside. There are two major problems with bringing daylight indoors. First, on a sunny day, if the window is facing east, south or west there will be a time of day when the beams of sunlight may be too bright and cause glare. That can be handled using shades or louvers. A bigger problem is the brightness of daylight diminishes rapidly the further you get from a window. This phenomenon, called the "inverse square law of light", significantly limits the usefulness of daylight within buildings.

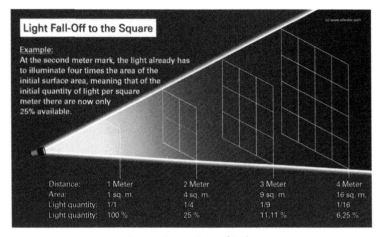

Distance:	1 Meter	2 Meter	3 Meter	4 Meter
Area:	1 sq. m.	4 sq. m.	9 sq. m.	16 sq. m.
Light quantity:	1/1	1/4	1/9	1/16
Light quantity:	100 %	25 %	11,11 %	6,25 %

Inverse Square Law of Light.
(elixxier Software GmbH www.elixxier.com)

SCIENTIFIC ASIDE:
Inverse Square Law of Light

The easiest way to explain the inverse square law of light is to consider a room with a one-meter square window (approximately 3 feet 3 inches x 3 feet 3 inches). The photons of daylight that enter that window come from multiple directions and spread out as they cross the room. The farther they travel across the room the same number of photons illuminate an increasingly larger area, and therefore the brightness measured in photons per square meter per second progressively falls. One meter from the window, the photons will illuminate an area four times greater than the window (2 meters x 2 meters), and the light intensity drops to 25% of that measured at the window. Two meters from the window, the photons are spread out over an area nine times larger than the window (3 meters by 3 meters), and the light intensity drops to 11%. Three meters from the window, the area covered is sixteen times larger (4 meters by 4 meters), and the light intensity is reduced to about 6% of the original. In mathematical terms this law can be expressed as the light intensity is reduced by the inverse square of the distance from the light source, and this is true for any light source, including windows, light bulbs and fixtures.

This is the definition of the inverse square law you will find in physics textbooks or on the internet. It is technically correct, but it is not what happens in the real world. The inverse square law only applies to unrestricted space with no reflecting surfaces. If some of the photons of light from the window or lamp are reflected off other surfaces, such as floors, walls, and ceilings, this will add to the total

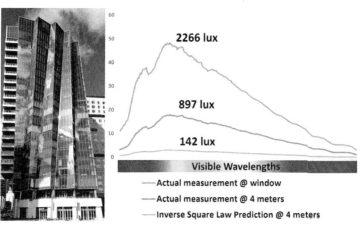

Measurements of indoor illumination at the north-facing windows and 4 meters from those windows of a building on the Boston waterfront demonstrate that light penetrates farther indoors than is predicted by the inverse square law of light.
(Copyright Circadian Light Research Center)

illumination you receive, and significantly reduce the effect of the inverse square law.

To demonstrate this, I visited one of the spectacular new buildings with huge picture windows on the Boston waterfront. Would the light coming in through those windows drop off with the square of the distance from the window?

To avoid the complications from beams of sunlight, I visited a north-facing unit at noon with the electric lights all switched off. First, I measured the light coming in from the window with my spectrophotometer pressed against the glass. It was only 2,266 lux, far below the 9,500 lux I measured facing north outdoors. The difference was due to the light-absorbing window glass, which appeared to have had a Visible Light Transmission (VLT) of about 24%.

Then I measured 4 meters back from the window where the Inverse Square Law would predict the illumination would fall to 6.25% of the window measurement, which would be 142 lux. Instead, my spectrophotometer measured 897 lux, which meant that the illumination at 4 meters away was only 40% less than the window measurement. The reason was that the reflection of window light, off the white walls, ceiling, and floor, redirected a lot of additional light photons towards my eyes and the spectrophotometer. Distance from the window is still an issue in interior daylighting, but less than that predicted by the Inverse Square Law.

Pre-Electric Architecture

"The history of architecture is the history of the struggle for light", Le Corbusier, the revolutionary architect, wrote in 1927.[142] Before electric light, every building had to rely on natural light during the day since candles, oil lamps, and fires were impractical and too expensive to be used all day long. It was

a constant struggle to balance the excessive glare from beams of direct sunlight on sunny days, with the challenge that the brightness of light diminished rapidly on cloudy days the further you stood from a window.

In the pre-electric era, most people spent their days outdoors and only returned to their homes at night. So, daylighting the home was not an issue, and windows were better kept small to exclude the rain and snow and reduce heat loss in winter. For people who did spend their days indoors, windows had to be large and building interiors narrow, or built with internal atriums and courtyards so that their occupants were never too far from the daylight entering a window.

Larger public gathering spaces, such as temples and cathedrals, used skylights or "clerestory" windows high above the surrounding rooftops, to bring in the daylight.[143] A classic example is the Pantheon, the ancient temple built in Rome in 127 AD, which is still in use today. This circular building, 142 feet across, is topped

The ancient Pantheon built in Rome in 127 AD is illuminated by a circular opening in the roof called the oculus. (iStock.com/fokkebok)

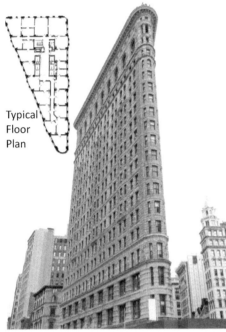

Typical
Floor
Plan

The Flatiron building in New York was built to maximize the use of daylight by having all interior space illuminated by tall windows, except for a small interior core.
(Adapted from iStock.com/resulmuslu)

by an enormous dome with a 27-foot (8.3 meter) opening, in its center called the "oculus". On a sunny day, a circular sunbeam moves around the interior space, marking the time of the day. On a cloudy day a dimmer, more diffuse, daylight fills the space.[144]

Skylights and high windows only work well in single-story buildings, or buildings with central atriums providing daylight to several floors.

When New York and Chicago started to build skyscrapers of increasing height in the 1870s, architects recognized that space more than 20 - 25 feet away from a window would be difficult or impossible to rent.[145] These early skyscrapers were narrow buildings so that the amount of space illuminated by natural light was maximized. Ceilings were high on each floor and windows were tall to bring in more daylight. [146] Most of these buildings were 15 stories or less and have since been demolished and replaced by even taller skyscrapers. However, the Flatiron building in Manhattan remains an example of a building designed before the widespread use of electric light. Except for a small inner core, all the rooms are illuminated by natural light.

Electric Light in Deep Space

The introduction of fluorescent lights and air conditioning in the 1950s ushered in the era of "deep-plan" buildings. These freed architects from relying on daylight for illumination, and windows for ventilation. Construction costs were reduced by significantly increasing the amount of floor space within a set of outer walls and using electric light to illuminate that interior space.

The executives and senior managers got the windowed offices on the perimeter, but most of the workforce found themselves in windowless cubicle farms under twilight levels of electrical illumination. When the oil embargos of the 1970s raised concerns about the accelerating cost of energy, building owners responded by dimming electric lights to save on the utility bill.[147] The math seemed simple. If you could replace 300 lux of light with fixtures providing 100 lux, the electric bill for lighting would be reduced by two-thirds.

This astonishingly short-sighted de-lamping of the workplace caused increased drowsiness and decreased alertness on the job, depressing mood and reducing performance and workforce productivity. In one study conducted in 2020 the benefit of windowed offices with plenty of blue-rich daylight boosted cognitive performance on decision-making tasks by 42% compared to offices with blinds blocking the windows.[148] The costs of employee productivity loss in the windowless offices thus far exceeded any savings obtained on the electric utility bill.

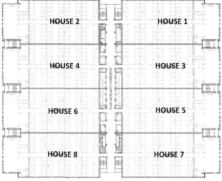

The proposed design and floor plan of Munger Hall with 4.500 windowless bedrooms at the University of California, Santa Barbara (University of California, Santa Barbara, Scoping Hearing on Munger Hall).

Venturing Too Far into Deep Space

The height of ignorance about the value of daylight was displayed when Charles T Munger, a billionaire investor and Berkshire Hathaway executive, proposed in 2021 to donate a self-designed dormitory for students at the University of California, Santa Barbara. Munger Hall was designed to house 4,500 students in windowless bedrooms in the interior of a vast 1.7-million-square-foot, 11-story building.[149]

After the project was announced, there was an enormous pushback, with the building being called "a giant windowless prison" and "a recipe for student depression". The UC Santa Barbara's architectural consultant, Dennis McFadden, resigned in protest saying, "An ample body of documented evidence shows that interior environments with access to natural light, air, and views to nature improve both the physical and mental well-being of the occupants." Finally in 2023 the mounting criticism led the university to cancel the project and return the $200 million donation to Charles Munger.[150]

The value of daylight for promoting good health is hardly a new idea. As Florence Nightingale wrote in her textbook on nursing in 1860, "It is the unqualified result of all my experience with the sick, that second only to their need of fresh air is their need of light; that, after a closed room, what hurts them most is a dark room."[151] Being close to the window and exposed to daylight speeds up the recovery of hospital patients and boosts the health of office workers. Employees in windowed offices exposed to an average of 1,000 lux of daylight get 45 minutes extra sleep per night as compared to workers in windowless offices exposed to 390 lux of electric light.[152] The timing of the daylight also matters. Depressed patients admitted to hospital rooms facing southeast, where they get plentiful morning light, are discharged twice as quickly as those admitted to northwest-facing rooms with no morning sunlight.[153]

Most regulatory initiatives about daylighting have been concerned with saving energy by dimming electric lights or switching them off when there is adequate daylight from windows. For example, California Title 24 requires electric fixtures near windows to be equipped with automatic dimmers when daylight from windows is bright.[154]

But now, finally, there is some momentum towards recognizing the health benefits of sunlight. After ten years of drafting, the European Union published in 2018 the European Standard for Daylighting EN 17037, which defines the quantity and quality of natural daylight that occupants should experience.[155] According to this standard daylight should provide a minimum of 300 lux over 50% of the building space for more than half the daylight hours in the year without using artificial lighting.

Piping in Daylight

A lot of engineering ingenuity is being applied to getting daylight deep into buildings, especially in the tropics where sunlight is plentiful and electric supply unreliable.[156] Using outdoor light collectors, equipped with mirrors or other reflecting sources to focus and concentrate the light beam, and light pipes or fiber optic cables, sunlight can be transported deep into interior spaces.[157] These systems can work well during daytime hours on a sunny day, but have to cope with the constantly moving position of the sun, and the impact of cloudy weather where light levels can fall by 90% or more. So, these systems have to be supplemented by electric light.

Illumination Not Adequately Blue

Outdoors during the daytime, in virtually any weather, there is sufficient light of every visible wavelength, including the blue photons, which are so essential for synchronizing and strengthening our circadian rhythms. But indoors where light levels are more than 100 times less, we need to pay attention to the blue content of light. Illumination that is perfectly adequate for vision and performing our daily activities, may not contain enough blue to be healthy during the daytime, and often has far too much blue content at night.

So efficient are our eyes that we can adapt our vision to a wide variety of lighting conditions, and barely notice the change. We can see our surroundings sufficiently to navigate safely over a million-fold range from less than 0.1 lux of moonlight to 100,000 lux of sunlight, and adapt well enough from one condition to another within minutes. However, we cannot easily judge how much circadian blue light we are receiving.

SCIENTIFIC ASIDE:
Flexible Vision is a Priority

We achieve this enormous flexibility in vision by using two systems. First, by automatically varying the diameter of our pupils, depending on the brightness of the light falling on our eyes, the amount of light entering the eye can be reduced or increased by up to 16-fold.[158] In dim light, the pupil is fully dilated, letting in as many photons as possible. But as the brightness of light increases, the pupil is progressively constricted, reducing the number of photons that would otherwise enter. Under normal conditions, this pupil reflex is most sensitive to green light at about 540nm.[159] This system's priority, therefore, is to regulate the amount of green-rich light we are exposed to optimize our visual perception, but not to optimize the amount of blue light we need to keep our circadian clocks in sync.[160]

The second system utilizes two types of photoreceptors in our eyes that enable us to see the world around us. The rods in our retina are optimized for seeing under dim light and the cones are designed for optimal vision when the light is bright.

However, these two visual systems are not tuned to optimize the circadian blue photons that are detected by the ipRGC melanopic receptors that synchronize our circadian clocks.

Survival of the fittest thus favored the immediate advantages of optimizing our vision over the longer-term advantage of optimizing our health by keeping our circadian clocks in sync. Without that emphasis on maximizing vision, our ancestors would more easily fall victim to the Sabre tooth tigers and other predators in their world. They would also miss opportunities to catch and gather food for themselves. Fortunately, there is enormous redundancy in our circadian daylight-moonlight blue-wavelength detecting system because the contrast in the brightness of light between natural day and night is so great. It was only when we began spending over 90% of our time indoors under twilight conditions that the design of our circadian system has shown its limitations.

We have chosen to live indoors under a constant electrical twilight that is very different from the natural cycle of blue-rich days and blue depleted nights. The use of electric lighting confers enormous advantages of convenience and flexibility, but we can only afford this luxury if we make sure we are still receiving the blue-rich day, no-blue night, signal that our circadian clocks require to preserve our health.

In this chapter, you have learned:

1. Getting outside and being exposed to natural blue-rich daylight for an hour each day, especially during the morning hours, provides considerable benefits for your health and well-being

2. It is easier to get sufficient natural light within buildings to improve your health if you are close to a window because the intensity of indoor light falls rapidly the farther you are from a window.

3. We can see the world around us under a wide range of lighting levels, but our vision does not permit us to be consciously aware of how much blue light we are receiving.

7

Tuning to the Right Wavelength

Which blue color wavelengths, and what dosage, do we need to sync our circadian clocks? We must know this to design healthy circadian lights.

Just like adjusting the dial to get your favorite FM or AM radio station, electric lights must be tuned to the correct circadian blue wavelengths to ensure a clear day-night signal. In the natural outdoor world, where there is such a large contrast between the brightness of daylight and the dimness of moonlight, the circadian signal is extremely strong. But now that we spend most of our days and nights under twilight levels of indoor lighting, the daily light-dark time cues can become very weak, so tuning to the correct circadian-synchronizing blue wavelengths becomes critical.

After we demonstrated in 1981 that human circadian rhythms were entrained by the daily light-dark cycle, (see Chapter 2: *Goodbye Milky Way)*, I assumed, like everyone else, that any sufficiently bright visible light would be effective in synchronizing the human circadian clock.[161] But with the arrival of the new millennium in 2000 our understanding of the impact of light on circadian clocks and health radically changed.

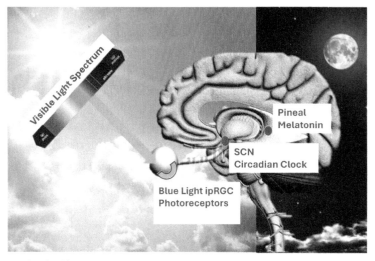

The sky-blue wavelengths in visible light are detected by melanopsin-containing ipRGC blue light detectors in the retina of the eye. Sky-blue light is over 25 times more effective in resetting the SCN circadian clock than the full spectrum of white light. (Brain image from Dreamstime.com/Decade3d)

Meanwhile, everyone else was paying attention to a non-event. At the stroke of midnight on January 1st, 2000, there was widespread fear that vital computer systems across the world would fail. The early computer programmers used two digits for dates to save computer memory, so 1998 was coded 98 and 1999 was 99. There was panic that this so-called Y2K bug would read 00 as the year 1900 and would cause havoc in air traffic control, military and telecommunications systems. Countries like the USA, UK, and Australia invested millions of dollars fixing the Y2K bug. Russia invested virtually nothing.

Australia recalled almost all of its embassy staff from Russia prior to January 1, 2000, over fears of what might happen. But absolutely nothing happened.[162]

In contrast, the new millennium was a momentous time for the science of healthy lighting. Three ground-shifting breakthroughs were reported in 2000-2001.

1. Light exposure at night was shown to be carcinogenic. Three independent studies, as we discussed in Chapter 1: *Edison's Cancer Epidemic*, showed a ~ 50% increased risk of breast cancer in women exposed to light at night. This opened the door to our current understanding that many diseases are caused by exposure to the wrong light at the wrong time.

2. Light at the blue end of the spectrum was shown to be more effective than longer-wavelength light in suppressing the nocturnal rise of melatonin. This has evolved into an understanding of the different "spectral recipes" required for our day and night "light diet."

3. A blue-sensitive photopigment called melanopsin was discovered in the ipRGC receptors in the eye that are responsible for synchronizing circadian clocks. This has led to a detailed understanding of the eye and brain clock mechanisms that govern our response to the Earth's day-night rotation.

An avalanche of scientific studies and research papers expanded on these breakthrough findings. As always happens, some apparently conflicting results has led to some confusion. It took another twenty years to sort this out and get a clear scientific consensus among the scientists in this field, as discussed in Chapter 5: *You Have the Right to Healthy Light.*

So, I have a word of advice for the non-scientist trying to understand the science of healthy circadian light. It is dangerous to rely on just one or two scientific articles, or news reports, which may lead you astray – instead you must look at the synthesis of all this science placed in context, which I will try to do here.

The Impetus to Design Healthier Lights

By the early 2000s the evidence was rapidly accumulating that exposure to light at night was associated with an increased risk of breast cancer. This culminated in the World Health Organization's finding in 2007 that light exposure on the night shift was carcinogenic, as discussed in Chapter 1: *Edison's Cancer Epidemic*.[163] At that time, my consulting firm CIRCA-DIAN®, which I founded in 1983, had over half the Fortune 500 companies as clients. Because we advised them on health and safety on the night shift, we were frequently asked what should be done about the lights at night, given the evidence that they may be causing increased rates of breast cancer and other diseases.

So, when in 2001 two well-respected groups of scientists published papers showing that shorter-wavelength light at the blue end of the spectrum appeared to be more effective than longer-wavelength light in synchronizing circadian clocks, it got my attention. This meant that electric light could potentially be tailored by making it blue-rich for daytime use and blue-depleted for nighttime use.

It became clear that we needed to explore whether healthier lights could be designed. But there was a problem. The published research on the sensitivity of circadian clocks to different wavelengths of light showed that while the peak sensitivity was in the blue, a broad range of violet and green wavelengths also had powerful effects. If we had to exclude all violet, blue and green from white light at night, the resultant light would be a yellow-orange color that could be undesirable unless preparing for sleep.

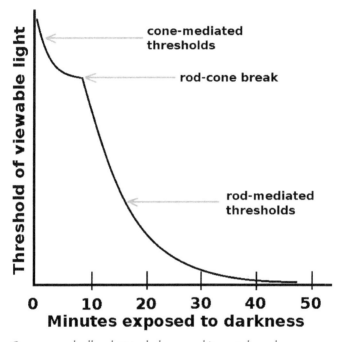

Our eyes gradually adapt to darkness, and it can take an hour or more to achieve a fully dark-adapted state where we rely solely on the rods in our retina for vision. (Public Domain Image, Christopher S. Baird).

The Dark-Adapted and the Light-Adapted Eye Behave Differently

Our invention of attractive white healthy circadian lighting hinged recognizing the differences between the dark-adapted and the light-adapted human eye.

Dark-adapted and light-adapted are two very different conditions. When we switch off the lights, or walk outside into the dark at night, our eyes gradually adapt so we can see under the very dim conditions of moonlight or starlight. We only become fully dark-adapted when we have been in pitch darkness for several hours. The cones in our retina can dark-adapt in 10 minutes, but the rods in the retina that provide our dim light vision can take a couple of hours to fully adapt to darkness. Astronomers know this well. They allow their eyes to fully dark-adapt for several hours before they gaze at the stars to maximize the sensitivity of their night vision.[164]

When we are first exposed to light, our vision takes a few minutes to adjust, but our color detection can take an hour more to adapt to the fully light-adapted state. (iStock.com/stevanovicigor)

When you first switch on the lights in the morning or open the curtains to let in daylight after sleeping in the dark at night, your dark-adapted eyes are initially blinded by the light. Your eyes then gradually adjust to normal daylight vision, becoming fully light-adapted over a couple of hours.

Photobiology, which is the scientific study of the effects of

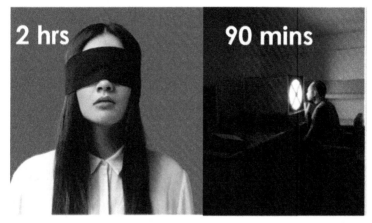

The classic photobiology experiments using blindfolded dark-adapted subjects who are then exposed to 30-90 minutes of monochromatic light. Violet, blue and green lights can suppress melatonin initially. However, after 2 hours only blue light is effective. (iStock.com/LightFieldStudios and Spitschan et al 2019)

light on the eye, typically utilizes the dark-adapted eye because that is the most reproducible resting state. And so that was how the sensitivity of the circadian system to the different color wavelengths of light was first studied. These dark-adapted experimental conditions led to the initial conclusion that a broad range of violet, blue, and green wavelengths could reset the human circadian clock.

SCIENTIFIC ASIDE:
Spectral Sensitivity in the Dark

Professor Josephine Arendt's group at the University of Surrey, England, and Professor George (Bud) Brainard's team at Thomas Jefferson University in Philadelphia, both made sure their human subjects were fully dark-adapted by sitting them in a dark room and blindfolding them for approximately two hours. That way their eyes would be most sensitive in responding to light. To further increase sensitivity, they put anticholinergic drops into the volunteers' eyes, so their pupils were dilated and would not constrict in response to light. Each person was then exposed to monochromatic (single wavelength) light for up to 90 minutes in the late evening to determine how much the melatonin hormone levels were suppressed.

These studies compared violet (420, 424 nm) versus several different blues (440, 460, 480, 496 nm) versus several greens (505, 520, 530, 555 nm) versus yellow (575 nm) versus orange (600 nm) light. Based on all this data, the Arendt team concluded the peak sensitivity of the circadian system was at 459 nm, and the Brainard team concluded the peak was at 464 nm, both in the royal blue part of the spectrum.[165] But their results also suggested a broad sensitivity to violet, blue, and green wavelengths.

Sky Blue Light Receptor

But something did not add up. The melanopsin photopigment that was identified in the ipRGC blue light detectors in the eye was more sensitive to ~ 480 nm sky blue light than to the ~ 460 nm royal blue wavelengths suggested by the Arendt and Brainard studies.

SCIENTIFIC ASIDE:
The Spectral Sensitivity of Melanopsin

At around the same time in the early 2000s, Professor Ignacio Provencio at the Uniformed Services

University of Health Sciences in Bethesda, Maryland, discovered the specialized photopigment called melanopsin that is responsible for detecting the light signals that synchronize circadian clocks.[166] The blue light sensitive melanopsin was found in the retinal ganglion cells in the eye which are directly connected to the master circadian pacemaker in the suprachiasmatic nucleus. Subsequent work in 2013 by Professor Robert Lucas and his colleagues at the University of Manchester, England, showed that the peak sensitivity of the human melanopsin photopigment was to sky-blue light at 479 nm.[167]

Eureka Moment

I was pondering how to create acceptable white lights for the nighttime workplace when one of my colleagues at CIRCADIAN, Dr Acacia Aguirre, an M.D., Ph.D. researcher, walked into my office. She asked whether I had seen a paper just published by Professor Robert Casper's group at the University of Toronto, Canada. It showed that the circadian system responded to blue wavelengths but not to green, meaning that the critical circadian light signal was a narrower band of light wavelengths than was previously thought.

The eureka moment came when I realized there was a critical difference between the previous research by Professors Jo Arendt's and Bud Brainard's groups and Professor Robert Casper's studies. The previous studies had all been done in the dark with fully dark-adapted subjects. In contrast, Professor Casper's studies had been done under standard room lighting with subjects fully adapted to bright indoor white light.

SCIENTIFIC ASIDE:
Filtering Wavelengths
Under Light-Adapted Conditions

Professor Casper and his colleagues created special eyewear that filtered out only the blue and violet wavelengths below <485 nm (<10% transmission) and allowed all the green, yellow, orange, and red wavelengths to reach the eyes of their human subjects. When they sat under bright fluorescent office lighting all night (600-1,000 lux tabletop), the melatonin rhythm was highly suppressed. However, when the subjects wore the blue & violet light filtering glasses, the melatonin rhythm was fully restored to the levels seen under darkness at night.[168] This meant that green light had no effect, and the circadian signal that suppressed melatonin was comprised of only blue (and possibly violet) light.

In the workplace, you are typically fully light-adapted because by the time you have woken up, got dressed, had breakfast, and commuted to your job, your eyes have fully adjusted to light. Therefore, workplace lighting should be geared for the eye's light-adapted state. Lighting at home in the first hour or so after awakening is a different matter. Under those conditions, a broader range of violet, blue, and green wavelengths can reset your biological clock, as was shown by the research teams led by Professor Brainard and Professor Arendt.

But we spend most of our daytime in a fully light-adapted state. The circadian clock's sensitivity to violet light and green light mostly disappears within two hours after switching on the lights in the morning. After that, for the rest of the day, while we are awake and going about our daily activities, even when working an overnight shift, as in Professor Casper's studies, our circadian clocks are only sensitive to the blue wavelengths in light. This unique response to blue light lasts as long as the lights remain on.

Blue Dosage is the Key

To create electric lights that would synchronize and strengthen circadian rhythms during the day and protect us from circadian disruption after sunset, we needed to know the precise dosages of blue light required. The key questions are:

1. What is the minimum dosage of blue light during daytime hours to synchronize our circadian clocks and keep us healthy?

2. What is the maximum safe dosage of blue light permissible in the evenings and at night that will prevent circadian disruption and the ill health caused by light at night?

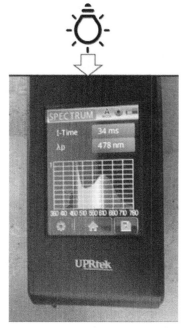

To answer these questions, we first needed to define the precise wavelengths of blue light that synchronize human circadian clocks, and then we needed to determine

A screenshot of a handheld spectrophotometer that has been pointed at a light designed for circadian daytime use. Note the peak at 480 nm in the blue wavelengths. (Copyright Circadian Light Research Center)

the required dosages of those specific blue wavelengths. A key instrument used for making these measurements is the spectrophotometer.

With a handheld spectrophotometer, a device about the size of an iPhone, you can easily measure all the visible wavelengths in a light. Point the device at a light, or your eye field of view, and press a button, and the data is captured and stored.

The spectral power distribution is plotted on the screen so you can quickly see how much of each color wavelength is contained in a light. On another screen you can see various measurements such as the intensity of the light in lux or foot-candles, and the coordinated color temperature (CCT). You can also download the data on the irradiance (the amount of radiant energy) of each wavelength falling on the spectropho-tometer (measured in microwatts per square centimeter – ab-breviated as $\mu W/cm^2$) into a computer and analyze it. Thus, a spectrophotometer allows you to quickly determine the blue dosage any light emits.

The Narrow Sky-Blue Signal

In Chapter 3: *Clockwork Blue*, you learned that a band of sky-blue wavelengths conveys the knowledge of time of day and night to the animal kingdom, whether living deep below the sea or land-based. To design electric lights that mimic the timing signals of "Mother Nature" for humans we needed to know the precise range of effective blue wavelengths and the wavelength with the peak sensitivity.

Typically, when we use electric light, we are fully light-adapted. So, it was essential to determine the circadian active blue wavelengths in the light-adapted state, as op-posed to the dark-adapted conditions previously studied by photobiologists.

SCIENTIFIC ASIDE:
Identifying the Circadian Blue Signal

Our goal was to identify the specific blue wavelengths that provided the circadian timing cues in people who were fully light-adapted and were living and working under normal lighting conditions.

We started by creating special filters that would remove narrow wavelength bands from the white light spectrum. We conducted a series of overnight studies with fully light-adapted volunteers exposed all night to electric lights fitted with these different wavelength filters. This enabled us to narrow down the critical circadian-active wavelengths to a range of blue light between 430 nm and 500 nm.[169] This meant that all the conventional blue-pump LED lights with a large spike of blue typically between 440-460 nm were fully capable of suppressing melatonin and disrupting circadian clocks.

The next step in our studies used an important feature of LED lights. With LEDs you can engineer almost any spectrum you want with different amounts of violet, blue, green, yellow, orange and red wavelengths. As we will discuss in Chapter 8, *Creating Healthy Light*, you can build LED lights that appear white using many different permutations and combinations of these different color wavelengths. This permitted us to compare the suppression of overnight melatonin by very different LED lights, all delivering white light at the same brightness (lux) level. Because the mix of wavelengths differed for each LED light, we could tease out which individual wavelengths were the most effective at suppressing melatonin and impacting circadian clocks.

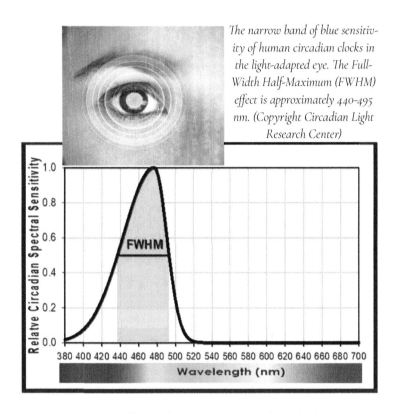

The narrow band of blue sensitivity of human circadian clocks in the light-adapted eye. The Full-Width Half-Maximum (FWHM) effect is approximately 440-495 nm. (Copyright Circadian Light Research Center)

In 2020, we published our discovery of the light-adapted circadian blue signal. As shown in the Figure, it was a narrow band of sky-blue wavelengths.[170] We calculated the peak effect at 477 nm, which is very close to the peak 479 nm sensitivity of melanopsin. This confirmed that we were studying the signal that triggers the non-visual pathway, which synchronizes circadian clocks. In 2022, researchers at the Division of Sleep and Circadian Disorders at the Brigham and Women's Hospital in Boston confirmed our finding that the peak sensitivity of light-adapted people was close to 480 nm (480 +/- 3 nm) for both melatonin suppression and for resetting the circadian clock.[171]

Since 480 nm sky blue light is so effective, you need much less of it to reset circadian clocks than polychromatic white light, where the energy is distributed across multiple violet, blue, green, yellow, orange, and red wavelengths. A monochromatic 480 nm pure blue light delivering $12\mu W/cm^2$ to a person's eyes has been shown to have almost the same circadian clock resetting power as 3000 $\mu W/cm^2$ of broad-spectrum white light. The fact that pure blue light delivered the same effect with less than 1% of the energy of the white light tells us that virtually all the circadian action is in the blue wavelength band.

We now knew that the peak sky-blue signal is at approximately 480 nm and 75% of the effect is in the ~ 440-495 nm range. Therefore, these blue wavelengths must be provided by light during the day and removed from electric light during the night.

What is the Effective Dose of Circadian Blue Light?

Now that we knew the key wavelengths of sky-blue light, we needed to determine the minimum dose that would be effective during the day to synchronize and strengthen our human circadian rhythms. We also needed to know the maximum tolerable dose of blue light at night that would ensure our circadian clocks are not disrupted by light at night. That way, we can design healthy circadian electric lighting that meets our objective of supporting, and not disrupting, our human circadian timing system.

DAYTIME CIRCADIAN BLUE THRESHOLD

First Author	Date	Test Condition	Biomedical Effect	At eye 440-495 nm µW/cm²	Result
Wakamura	2001	3000 lux eye 5000K fluorescent	Improved sleep length and increased daytime activity	188.59	CIRCADIAN STABILITY
Takasu	2006	5000 lux eye 4100K fluorescent	Synchronized circadian rhythms, increased melatonin, and daytime alertness	184.56	
Boubekri	2014	1000 lux eye Daylight window	Improved sleep length and quality, improved vitality & activity	78.01	
Viola	2008	186 lux eye 17000K fluorescent	Improved sleep, mood, alertness and performance	23.74	
Najjar	2014	171 lux eye 17000K fluorescent	Synchronized circadian rhythms; improved sleep, cognitive performance & mood	21.82	
					20 µW/cm²
Boubekri	2014	380 lux eye fluorescent no window	Disrupted shorter sleep; lower vitality; reduced activity	14.03	CIRCADIAN DISRUPTION
Wakamura	2001	175 lux eye Daylight North facing window	Reduced sleep length and decreased daytime activity	13.65	
Viola	2008	253 lux eye 4000K Fluorescent	Impaired sleep, mood, alertness and performance	9.32	
Najjar	2014	165 lux eye 4100K fluorescent	Disrupted circadian sleep rhythms; impaired cognitive performance & mood	5.91	
Takasu	2006	10 lux eye 4100K fluorescent	Disrupted circadian rhythms, decreased melatonin, and daytime sleepiness	0.37	

The daytime circadian blue threshold dose (µW/cm2) for the beneficial effects of light (Copyright Circadian Light Research Center)

EVENING/NOCTURNAL CIRCADIAN BLUE THRESHOLD

First Author	Date	Test Condition	Biomedical Effect	At eye 440 495 nm µW/cm²	Result
Rahman	2011	513 lux eye 5000K fluorescent unfiltered	Suppressed melatonin, disrupted BMal1, Per2 gene expression	21.57	CIRCADIAN DISRUPTION
Munch	2006	12.1 µW/cm² eye monochromatic 460 nm blue	Altered EEG sleep	12.10	
Moore-Ede	2023	259 lux eye 4000K LED	Suppress & shift melatonin, increased appetite & insulin resistance	12.00	
Kayaba	2014	12.1 µW/cm² eye monochromatic 465 nm blue	Increased drowsiness and energy metabolism, without sleep changes	6.73	
				2 µW/cm²	
Rahman	2011	439 lux eye 5000K fluorescent < 480nm filtered	Restored melatonin, BMal1, Per2 gene expression	1.51	CIRCADIAN STABILITY
Moore-Ede	2023	299 lux eye 3300K violet peak low blue	Restored melatonin, appetite, and insulin resistance	1.37	

The nocturnal circadian blue threshold dose (µW/cm2) for the harmful effects of light (Copyright Circadian Light Research Center)

We took advantage of multiple published studies that have compared the effects of bright-blue rich light with the effects of dim blue-depleted light on various measures of health. We divided these studies into daytime and nighttime studies and used them to determine the respective thresholds for daytime effectiveness and for nocturnal health and safety.

The only light that matters for the circadian effect is the blue light that enters the eye ("blue corneal irradiance"). The measurements used in traditional lighting design such as desktop illumination in lux or foot-candles, the correlated color temperature (CCT), or color rendering index (CRI) are not helpful in this regard.

We concluded from these studies (summarized in the charts below) that:

1. The minimum threshold level of blue content required for effective daytime lighting (sunrise to sunset) is 20 $\mu W/cm^2$ of 440-495 nm circadian blue light.

2. The maximum safe threshold level of blue content for evening and night lighting (sunset to sunrise) is 2 $\mu W/cm^2$ of 440-495 nm circadian blue light.

As we will discuss more fully in Chapter 10 *Becoming a Smart Consumer of Light*, in practical terms, assuming typical indoor illumination levels, circadian lighting fixtures should provide:

1. Less than 2% circadian blue content during evening and night hours, and

2. More than 20% circadian blue content during daytime hours.

SCIENTIFIC ASIDE:
Thresholds of Blue Exposure

To determine these day and night thresholds we analyzed the relative power of each wavelength ("spectral power distribution") in the white lights used in each study, and calculated the total irradiance from blue light in the 440-495 nm range.

We discovered that during the day, the positive, healthy effects of light were seen whenever the 440-495 nm circadian blue light irradiance dose exceeded 20 $\mu W/cm^2$. In contrast, all the adverse effects of sleep disruption, reduced alertness and impaired performance occurred when the daytime blue light irradiance dose was below 20 $\mu W/cm^2$.[172]

During the night the harmful effects of melatonin suppression, sleep disruption, glucose intolerance, and gene disruption were seen when the blue irradiance was above 6 $\mu W/cm^2$, and circadian disruption was prevented when the blue irradiance was less than 2 $\mu W/cm^2$.[173] Since there is significant melatonin suppression with blue doses between 2 $\mu W/cm^2$ and 6 $\mu W/cm^2$, it is best to play safe and set the threshold for acceptable blue light levels at night at 2 $\mu W/cm^2$.

Light is like a pharmaceutical drug. It must have the proper chemical composition (wavelength) and the correct dose (eye-level blue irradiance) to have the desired therapeutic effect. So, to ensure human health and well-being, electric lights must be designed to make sure that the circadian blue dosage is correct under the challenging indoor conditions of being 100 times dimmer during the day and 100 times brighter at night as compared to natural light.

How we can accomplish these goals is the subject of the next chapter, *Creating Healthy Light.*

In this chapter, you have learned:

1. Under normal indoor lighting conditions, most of the power to synchronize or disrupt the circadian system lies in the blue wavelengths between 440 nm and 495 nm.

2. During the day (especially during the morning hours), an average blue light eye dosage of more than 20 μW/cm^2 is required to ensure robust and synchronized circadian rhythms

3. During the night, after sunset, the eye dosage of blue light we are exposed to needs to be kept below 2 μW/cm^2 to ensure our circadian rhythms are not disrupted by light exposure at night

8

Creating Healthy Light

How to balance illumination quality with human health and productivity while providing true energy efficiency.

The Sun delivers abundant light across all visible wavelengths, providing ample illumination and healthy rays at zero energy cost, even on an overcast day. In comparison, electric light can only be a pale imitation of sunlight. Because of indoor glare and reflections, electric lighting must always be hundreds of times less bright and deliver considerably fewer photons than sunlight. Thus, the design of indoor electric light is always a compromise and a trade-off. It is simply not possible to deliver every wavelength of visible light with sufficient intensity to provide all the health benefits discussed in Chapter 4: *Human Light Interaction.*

When Thomas Edison developed the first mass-produced electric light bulbs in 1879, he had only one goal – providing reliable illumination that could replace candlelight and gaslight. He was not particularly concerned with energy efficiency

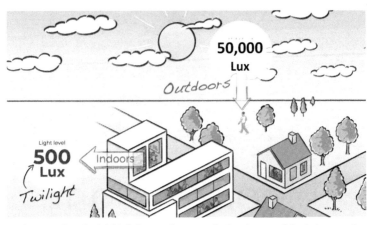

There is a hundred-fold difference between the brightness of daylight outside and the twilight levels of dimness in even a brightly lit indoor space. (Modified with permission from the Good Light Group).

and was unaware of the health-promoting properties of light. Over the past 100 years, the lighting industry has progressively improved the efficiency of lighting but has done very little to address the impact of light on human health.

The most common failure of modern electric lighting is that it is optimized to meet only the illumination and certain narrowly defined energy efficiency objectives while undermining human health and wellness. As we discussed in Chapter 1: *Edison's Cancer Epidemic* and Chapter 2: *Goodbye Milky Way*, the indiscriminate use of blue-enriched LED light in the evening and night hours has created an epidemic of obesity, diabetes, heart disease, breast cancer, and other endocrine-sensitive cancers.

So, it is necessary to prioritize four objectives in designing electric lighting to benefit humankind.

First Priority - Illumination:

There is no point in electric light if it doesn't provide adequate indoor illumination. Light must provide the visual acuity and color discrimination required to perform tasks and prevent slips and falls.

Second Priority - Human Health:

Since we live indoors more than 90% of the time, it is essential to build circadian supportive features into lighting and reverse the harm done by the indiscriminate use of blue-enriched light after sunset. To actively promote health, light must provide an adequate dose of sky-blue enriched light during the day to robustly synchronize the circadian timing system and must deliver blue-depleted light at night to prevent the harmful effects of circadian disruption.

Third Priority - Human Productivity:

It is a false economy to provide inexpensive light that depresses mood and alertness and impairs human performance and creativity. The costs of lost productivity are far greater than any saving on the utility bill. Therefore, light should stimulate human alertness, cognitive performance, and mood to optimize productivity and creativity.

Fourth Priority - Energy Efficiency:

Despite all their claims, the LED lights on the hardware store shelves today are really not energy efficient. Most LED manufacturers only measure energy efficiency in terms of visible light brightness – the so called "photopic illumination" metric dating back to 1924.[174]

Brightness measurements, such as 'lumens" and "lux," mainly focus on the green and yellow wavelengths. But other wavelengths critical for health, such as blue and red, have little impact on the lumens measurement.

Every light has a label indicating how many lumens it produces and how many watts of electricity it consumes. Unfortunately,

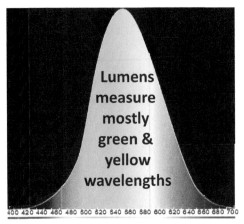

400 420 440 460 480 500 520 540 560 580 600 620 640 660 680 700

The relative contribution of different color wavelengths to the measured values of lumens and lux. The photopic luminosity function models how the human eye perceives brightness, which is predominately determined by green and yellow wavelengths. (Copyright Circadian Light Research Center)

energy efficiency regulations judge lights solely by their "lumens per watt", or luminous efficacy, which ignores the healthy properties of the light.

According to the US Environmental Protection Agency, in their own words, "Simply put, energy efficiency means using less energy to get the same job done."[175]

But if a light with a higher lumens/watt rating does not provide the same healthy light spectrum, it is not getting the same job done. So, it should not be claimed to be "energy-efficient".

As energy regulations progressively raise the lumens per watt target, they are forcing upon us lights that are just not healthy. Lumens per watt does not measure the energy efficiency of producing sky-blue light that will synchronize circadian clocks and protect health. And it does not measure the energy efficiency of the light in boosting human alertness and productivity. In short energy efficiency has only been measured in terms of Edison's goal of simply providing light so that people can see clearly in a dark room.

We are all fully aware of the global priority to reduce energy consumption and its associated carbon burden. But it is unacceptable to sacrifice human health and safety in the rush to regulate lighting to meet ill-conceived lumens/watt energy efficiency targets. We all want light sources that consume the fewest watts in generating light, but only if that light also achieves all other higher priorities. That is the true definition of energy efficiency.

Four Ways to Build Circadian Lights

When we first thought about how to create circadian electric lights that would provide room occupants with the required dosage of more than 20 µW/cm² sky-blue wavelengths during the day and less than 2µW/cm² during the evening hours, we realized there were several ways in which this could be done. Each had its pros and cons.

1. Dimming and Brightening Light

You could, in theory, vary light intensity more than 10-fold across the day to deliver adequate sky-blue wavelengths during the day and sufficiently reduce blue levels in the evening hours. But if you used conventional 3000 – 4000K LED lights to deliver enough sky-blue wavelengths, they would

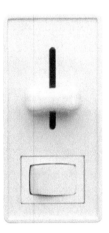

Some, but not all, lights can be dimmed, and there are limits to how much an LED light can be dimmed. (iStock.com/ PhotoMelon)

be uncomfortably bright during the day, causing glare and eyestrain. They would also be too dim in the evening hours, making it hard to read or do any detailed tasks. If you are getting ready for bed, that might not be an issue, but if your child is doing their homework, or you have to catch up with some work or hobbies in the evening, that could be a problem.

As the Correlated Color Temperature (CCT) of a light increases the color changes according to Planck's Law of blackbody radiators measured by the temperature in degrees Kelvin from 1,000K on left to 10,000K on right. Most people typically prefer their rooms lit with lights between 3,000 and 4,000 K. (iStock.com/Veronika Oliinyk)

2. Color-Tuning

The lighting industry has a long history of developing lights with different correlated color temperatures (CCT), primarily for aesthetic reasons. Starker bluish-white lights have higher CCT values, and softer yellowish-white lights have lower color temperatures. But just varying the CCT across the day doesn't qualify as effective circadian lighting unless it delivers the required sky-blue dosages. It is possible to build color-tuning lights that provide the necessary circadian day and night amounts of sky-blue light. However, to deliver more than 20 $\mu W/cm^2$ sky-blue wavelengths during the day, you must use harsh bluish 6500K light And to provide less than $2\mu W/cm^2$ blue during the evening hours, you must use orange-yellow 1800K light. Any lesser change in white color-tuning, for example, from 5000K during the day to 2700K in the evening, is just a placebo, and does not qualify as true circadian lighting, (unless accompanied by significant dimming at night and brightening during the day).

3. Filtering Light

Another approach to removing harmful sky-blue wavelengths during evening and nocturnal hours is to use filters that selectively block the critical circadian activating wavelengths. This is the approach used by blue-blocking glasses, which we will discuss in detail in Chapter 11: *When You Don't Control the Space.*

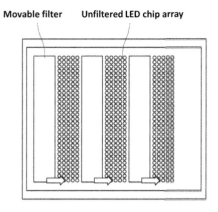

Movable filter   Unfiltered LED chip array

Schematic example of LED light fixture with LED chip arrays that emit blue-rich light during the day and moveable filters that remove all 440-495 mm blue wavelengths in the evening and at night. (Copyright Circadian Light Research Center)

We initially considered building lights with changeable filters that would cover the light source in the evening hours and then retract during the day. It can be complex mechanically, but more importantly, while filters can remove sky-blue light during the evening, they cannot add sky-blue light to boost the daytime circadian blue signal.

4. Spectral Engineering Light

The Nobel prize-winning invention of efficient LEDs (light-emitting diodes) made the precise spectral engineering of light possible. Spectral engineering is the selection of which color wavelengths to incorporate in a light and at what relative intensities. That way you can create light of precisely the right composition to achieve your objectives.

Most LED lights today have been spectrally engineered to achieve the greatest energy efficiency in provide per-

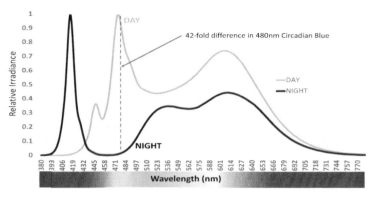

The spectrally-engineered circadian day and night LEDs we developed, which each provide white light, but with a 42-fold difference in the amount of circadian sky-blue light at the same perceptual brightness level..
(Copyright Circadian Light Research Center)

ceptually bright illumination at the lowest cost. That has resulted in lights that pump out large amounts of blue photons, largely because the most efficient electricity conversion to LED light occurs at approximately 450 nm blue. But as you are now well aware, that blue-rich light can be harmful at night. It is also suboptimal for daytime use because most LED lights are scarce in the sky-blue photons which are most effective for daytime synchronization of circadian clocks.

Fortunately, we can also use the same technology to convert the LED "sword" into "ploughshares", to use an analogy from the distant past. Since we want to prioritize good illumination, human health and productivity as well as energy efficiency, we can tailor make LEDs to meet these balanced objectives.

If the only purpose of light was to synchronize circadian clocks, then 480 nm sky-blue light would be most effective. If the only purpose of light was to be energy efficient at producing lumens, then 555 nm green light delivering up to 683 lumens per watt would consume the least electricity. If the only purpose of light was to stimulate you, and keep you awake, then 420 nm violet is best. But there is little point to providing electric light unless it also simulates some approximation of natural daylight which enables you to see clearly and perform your daily duties, tasks and hobbies.

A balance is clearly needed. But we do not have it with today's LED lights which are focused on providing aesthetics and lumens per watt efficacy at the lowest cost with little concern for human health.

Building Circadian LEDs

With the help of my engineering team and our LED manufacturing partners, we created LED lights that would meet all four of the key priorities listed above. Two types of LEDs were needed, one for daytime use from sunrise to sunset and the other for nighttime use from sunset to sunrise. We needed to select the right mix of light wavelengths (the spectral power distribution) that would provide circadian health, and productivity while also producing an attractive white light that would enable clear vision.

An LED module with rows of circadian day and circadian night LEDs in parallel. Each LED on the board is approximately 3 mm x 3 mm in size. (Copyright Circadian Light Research Center)

The key breakthrough was our finding that we could create an attractive warm white light for evening and night use, by replacing the blue LED chip with a violet LED chip in the

415-425 nm range.[176] The fully dark-adapted eye responds to violet for only the first hour, but violet light has minimal effects on circadian clocks for the rest of the waking day. Using a violet LED chip, we could balance the color spectrum in the absence of blue light, and create a light with an acceptable warm white color.

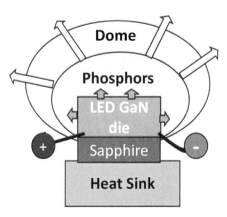

Schematic diagram of the components of an LED package. The LED die semiconductor (usually GaN) is grown on a substrate (usually sapphire). When electrically powered, the die emits blue light into a coating of phosphors, which converts much of the blue light into other spectral colors so that the LED package emits a balanced white light through a protective dome or lens. The heat sink helps conduct heat away from the LED so it can operate at a desired temperature.
(Copyright Circadian Light Research Center)

Like Edison, our first step was to immediately file patents to protect the rights to our invention of healthy day and night lights in the USA and internationally. Without these patents it would have been impossible to raise the money from investors. And we were glad we did this before contacting the manufacturing partners we needed to build the LED chips. Some of those we approached filed a flurry of patents as soon as they got wind of our idea.

But, because we were the first to the patent office, we had priority, and could protect our rights and obtain the investment needed to make healthy circadian lights a reality.

SCIENTIFIC ASIDE:
Spectral Engineering LEDs

The LED lights used for general indoor illumination are comprised of a set of small LED packages (typically about 3 mm x 3mm in size) each producing a dot of light. Multiple LED packages are usually mounted and wired together on a board to create an LED Module, which is the "light engine" for an LED light.

Two key elements in an LED package can be modified to spectrally engineer light. The first is the "die", which is a small chip of light-emitting semiconducting material on which the LED circuit is fabricated. The semiconductor is usually Gallium Nitride (GaN), Indium Nitride (InN), Aluminum Nitride (AlN), or Gallium Phosphide (GaP). The most common LED dies convert electricity into blue light with a peak wavelength of about 450 nm. Other common dies have blue peaks ranging between 440 and 470 nm. These blue dies are neither optimal for day or night lighting, so other specialized dies have had to be deployed.

The second adjustable element is the phosphor coating over the LED die, which converts much of the blue light from the die into green, yellow, and red wavelengths to create white light. Phosphors are solid fluorescent chemical compounds that absorb the LED chip's primary blue emission and undergo a Stokes shift, partially transforming the blue light into longer wavelengths. Dozens of phosphors can be used; one of the most common is YAG (Cerium-doped Yttrium Aluminum Garnet) which converts the blue die light into a green-yellow light with a peak at 550nm. The chemical composition of each phosphor determines the wavelengths of light emission, although significant amounts of the original die wavelength can leak through the phosphor layer. This is why the spectral power distribution of most LED lights shows a sharp blue peak around 450 nm (or the peak of whatever die is used) and a broad spectrum of other colors emitted from the phosphor mixture coating the LED.

Using the two adjustable features of LEDs, we were able to spectrally engineer LEDs for night use, which emitted virtually no sky-blue light, and less than 2% total blue content between 440nm-495nm. These night LEDs used a 415-425 nm violet die pump because, with special phosphor coatings, this enabled us to produce an attractive white light that did not disrupt circadian clocks while stimulating human alertness and performance. Remember from Chapter 4: *Human Light Interaction* that 420 nm violet is the most effective stimulator of alertness, even better than blue light.

Optimized LEDs for use in the daytime were built using an approximately 480 nm sky-blue die pump and specialized phosphors that also created attractive white light and emitted greater than 20% of the LED light in the circadian 440-495 nm blue band.

SCIENTIFIC ASIDE:
Color Temperature Tuning is Not Circadian

We were able to achieve a 10-15 fold contrast in the amount of circadian blue between day and night LEDs from spectral engineering with very little change in the correlated color temperature (CCT) of the light. We can produce 3300 K night LEDs with less than 2% blue content and 3500K day LEDs with greater than 20% blue. As we have discussed before this proves that CCT is not a reliable measure of the circadian impact of a light or its blue content. You can vary the CCT considerably without much change in blue content, and you can build lights with large differences in blue content with virtually the same CCT. So, lights that offer CCT color-tuning should not be called "circadian lighting" unless they also alter 440-495 nm blue content by an order of magnitude.

Developing Circadian LEDs

Of course, it wasn't that simple. It took several years of iterative development and testing to create circadian-friendly LED lights. The first partner we approached was Soraa, a Silicon Valley company founded by the Nobel Prize winner, Shuji Nakamura. Dr Nakamura had won his prize for developing the first blue-pump LED lights, and then at Soraa he had helped develop violet pump LEDs, which enhanced the colors in retail displays. We needed to use violet pump LEDs to avoid the devastating effects of blue light at night, so we asked Soraa to develop a number of trial night LEDs to our specifications which we could test for their circadian activity. Each trial LED had different peaks in the violet range and different bands of blue wavelengths removed.

As we will discuss more fully in the next chapter, Chapter 9: *Lights as Medical Devices*, we built a Circadian Light Research Center, to conduct medical and psychological performance testing with various trial lights to determine which had the most beneficial effect. With the spectral formula defined and verified, we could then look for a manufacturing partner.

To mass produce LEDs for circadian lights, we initially turned to Plessey Semiconductors, a specialty LED manufacturer in Plymouth, UK, the final port from where the pilgrims had embarked. They were able to build light engines for us with blue-rich day LEDs and blue depleted night LEDs. These initial circadian lights required making a compromise in energy efficiency. We achieved 50-60 lumens per watt with the night LED, which was less than most blue pump LEDs, which can deliver over 100 lumens per watt. But we more than made up with the health benefits we provided, as we will discuss in Chapter 9: *Lights as Medical Devices*.

The next product iteration was to see if we could achieve the health benefits with minimal compromise on energy efficiency. We assigned this task to Lumileds, one of the largest global LED manufacturers, formerly part of Philips Lighting. They were able to use their Luxeon technology to create day and night LED packages to our specifications of less than 2% blue night and greater than 20% blue day with energy efficiencies in the 125 – 145 lumens per watt range. This breakthrough removes any excuse for not using circadian lighting. In fact, you can argue it is unconscionable not to provide healthy lighting.

Keeping in Sync with Natural Day and Night

Manual controls are really not an option for circadian lighting. It takes too much attention to remember to switch the lighting from day to night and then back to the day setting. Some early circadian lighting installations in hospitals spent considerable effort redesigning the lighting, but provided a manual control panel on the wall. The nurses initially adjusted the panel to select the color of the lights they liked, but because they were too busy with their regular duties, they left the lights in a set position 24/7, totally defeating the purpose of circadian lighting.

Like your breathing, or heartbeat, circadian lights shouldn't require human intervention to keep time. Therefore, we designed a control board with a 10-year battery and a very precise clock chip that only drifted a few seconds per year. It could be set to local time according to the precise latitude and longitude of where the lights were installed. That way the control board would automatically transition the lights between day and night modes in sync with the rising and setting of the sun across the changing seasons of the year.

From LEDs to Light Fixtures

It is one thing to have LED packages and modules that can serve as circadian light engines. It is quite another to produce useable light fixtures and bulbs. Currently, lighting designers and architects can choose from an extraordinary diversity of lighting fixtures – provided they are willing to settle for conventional blue-pump LEDs. In a way, they have been spoiled. The typical large lighting manufacturer has millions of light fixture SKUs in their catalog from which a designer can choose. Each required a significant investment in time and engineering resources to create. So, one has to be highly selective in choosing which lighting fixture SKUs to convert to circadian lighting.

In 2016, we partnered with H. E. Williams, a lighting

manufacturer based in Missouri, to produce the first family of circadian lights. We built a set of troffers – the 2 x 2 feet, 2 x 4 feet and 1 x 4 feet ceiling fixtures commonly found in office buildings. With their automatic controls they switched between blue-rich day and blue-depleted night settings in sync with local sunrise and sunset.

We licensed the rights to build circadian lights using our intellectual property and technology to H.E. Williams, and to Acuity, the largest US lighting manufacturer, to enable a broader range of fixtures and bulbs to be developed and brought to market. Subsequently, we sold the IP to Korrus, the leaders in human light interaction, and they are now manufacturing circadian-friendly light bulbs and other circadian lighting fixtures.

In Chapter 9: *Lights as Medical Devices,* we will discuss the evidence that these circadian lights can have significant health benefits.

In this chapter, you have learned:

1. Spectrally engineered LEDs have been built, with a day LED that provides greater than 20% sky-blue rich light and a night LED that emits less than 2% blue light.

2. These LEDs have been built into light fixtures and light bulbs, which provide the correct dosages of blue light for day and night use.

3. Automatic controls in circadian lights ensure the day-night transitions occur in sync with dawn and dusk in the local longitude and latitude where the lights are installed.

Lights as Medical Devices

Consumers need to be aware of false claims about circadian lighting, and learn how to look for lights that truly have circadian benefits.

A case could be made that circadian lighting should be a medical device. Light fixtures and bulbs that provide ample circadian blue light during the day and keep circadian blue levels low at night have profound positive effects on human health and well-being. But circadian lighting has never been classified as a medical device, so we are faced with a Wild West of loose marketing claims. The idea of measuring the effects of electric lighting on biomarkers of human disease is foreign to most lighting manufacturers, and anathema to their marketing departments. So today, anyone can claim their lights are "circadian" with impunity and without risk of penalty.

It is therefore vital that architects, lighting designers and all lighting purchasers know the difference between true and false circadian lighting. The key is whether the claims about circadian lighting are "evidence-based" – i.e., supported by controlled scientific studies. Evidence-based is the key standard of modern health care and public health, and can, and should be, applied to health-promoting lighting products.

Lighting as an FDA Approved Medical Device

Should circadian lighting be approved as an FDA Class 2 Medical Device, or is it better to treat it as an FDA General Wellness Device? (Alamy.com/ Panther Media GmbH)

As we were developing circadian lighting that provided the precise dosages of sky-blue light levels to optimize health in day and night conditions, we wrestled with whether we should apply to the FDA to get our spectrally-engineered lights approved as Class 2 medical devices. If such circadian lighting systems were classified as Class 2 medical devices, they would require rigorous medical testing, and consumers would have confidence in the FDA-approved claims made by lighting manufacturers.

Our own internal preliminary medical trials of these circadian lights with human subjects, discussed later in this chapter, suggested that we should be successful in obtaining medical device approval for at least the following claims:

1. **Prevents Circadian Disruption**

2. **Reduces Diabetic Risk of Evening and Nighttime Light**

3. **Reduces Risk of Obesity**

These effects can be demonstrated in relatively short studies. However, other potential claims such as "Reduces the risk of breast cancer", would take too many years to study to be feasible as the initial FDA testable claims.

SCIENTIFIC ASIDE:
Medical Device Approval

The sale of medical devices that are intended to be used in the diagnosis, cure, or preventive treatment of a disease, with the intention to affect the structure of a human or animal body, is regulated in the USA by the Food and Drug Administration (FDA).[177] The main body regulating medical devices outside the USA is the EU's Medical Devices Regulation (MDR).[178] The European regulations and approval are accepted in most countries outside the USA,.

Most medical devices that affect how the body functions are placed in Class 2. Only the more invasive and implanted devices with significant risk are in Class 3. Class 1 is for general devices like bedpans and stethoscopes that do not treat an illness. The FDA requires proof of both safety and efficacy to approve Class 2 and Class 3 medical device claims.

Attractive as these advantages of FDA approval might be, there were significant reasons to think carefully about whether to proceed. First, obtaining FDA medical device approval would take considerable resources and time. There are multiple submissions and governmental regulatory reviews, and you must hire an independent Contract Research Organization

(CRO) to conduct the medical trials. Even if we were successful on the first round, it would take at least three million dollars and at least two years to get FDA approval of a simple set of specific marketing claims.

Second, all these FDA approval costs would have to be passed on in the pricing of circadian light fixtures and bulbs. We already faced an increased cost of circadian lighting compared to the mass market of unhealthy blue-pump LED lighting. Over the past ten years LED lights mass-produced in Asia have become a low-price commodity in our society. In addition, the Department of Energy and utility companies were providing discounts to get people to replace their lights with these blue-pump LEDs. In contrast, we had a new technology that didn't yet have the advantages of manufacturing scale and wasn't quite as energy efficient at delivering lumens as blue-pump LEDs.

Adding the incremental price necessary to recoup FDA approval costs to the already increased price of circadian lighting fixtures would only slow market adoption. Most FDA medical devices can be reimbursed through medical insurance, so the user does not directly see the impact on their wallet. However, it was unclear how medical insurance or DOE discounts would pay for circadian lighting. The result could be a very expensive product that we could not persuade people to buy, however good it would be for their health.

Ultimately, we decided not to proceed with Class 2 FDA medical device approval and settled on treating circadian lighting as a General Wellness Device.

Circadian Lighting as a General Wellness Device

In 2019, the Food and Drug Administration (FDA) issued a guidance document on the FDA's compliance policy for low-risk products that promote a healthy lifestyle, which they refer to as general wellness products.[179] These products must have low safety risk, and our circadian lights certainly complied. These General Wellness products may be sold without any FDA review or approval provided the manufacturer is responsible for the claims they make.

The FDA does not allow the manufacturer to claim that the device cures a specific disease or medical condition. However, claims can be made about improving general health and wellness through promoting a healthy lifestyle. Examples are claims about weight management, sleep management, mental acuity and alertness that don't mention any specific diseases, all of which are proven outcomes of using circadian lighting as we discuss later in this chapter.

In addition, a General Wellness Device can be claimed to promote a healthy lifestyle to help reduce the risk of certain chronic diseases or conditions. For example, we have the evidence from our research studies that I will discuss below, to support General Wellness claims about circadian lighting, such as:

1. **Removes Harmful Blue Wavelengths at Night, and Provides Healthy Blue-Rich Light During the Day**

2. **Supports Regular Circadian Rhythms, Which May Help to Reduce the Risk of Diabetes**

3. **Helps Control Excess Appetite at Night, Which May Help to Reduce the Risk of Obesity**

4. **Promotes a Healthy Sleep-Wake Cycle**

5. **Reduces Human Error and Improves Work Performance**

However, the problem with General Wellness Devices is that manufacturers can claim that their devices support general health and reduce disease risk without having any research studies or documented proof to back up their claims. This puts the onus back on the consumer to ask for and evaluate the evidence that any General Wellness Device does any good.

Thus, as a lighting consumer, you have to be smart in asking for evidence that the lights offered by a lighting contractor or online store truly support circadian health. So, let's review the evidence that you can ask for to back up any marketing claims you may see.

Three Ways to Know

Three aspects of circadian lighting can help you differentiate between true and false claims.

1. **Blue Content:** As we discussed in Chapter 7: *Tuning to the Right Wavelength*, manufacturers know, and should provide, the spectral power distribution (the relative power at each visible light wavelength) of the fixture or lamp. As a rough rule of thumb, at normal indoor lighting levels, the lights for evening and night use should have less than 2% circadian blue content (where the circadian blue range is 440 to 495 nm). And lights for daytime use should have more than 20% blue content in the same range.

2. **Day-Night Schedule:** Circadian lights, by definition, should change between day (high blue) and night (low blue) conditions. If the light is static, it is only suitable for either day or night use, depending on its blue content, but not for both day and night.

3. **Research Study Evidence:** The best proof of effective circadian lighting is that the spectral recipe for the light has been tested with people in controlled studies and has

been shown to have beneficial effects on health, safety, and well-being.

Biomarkers Used in Testing Circadian Lighting

To demonstrate the effects of circadian lighting on diseases like breast cancer or prostate cancer would require studying large populations of people over multiple years. Therefore, such prospective epidemiological studies are impractical in the short term for investigating whether a particular circadian lighting product is effective. However, we can instead use biomarkers of disease that indicate whether the lights are impacting processes that contribute to, or are closely associated with, a medical condition.

Examples of useful biomarkers which are all impacted by blue-rich light at night, and can be easily used to compare different lights are:

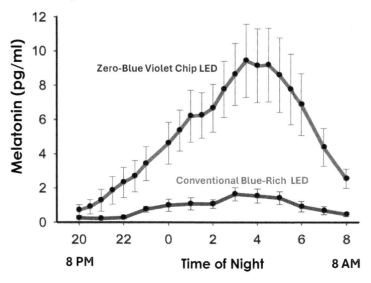

Bright blue-rich white LED light at night suppresses the rise of melatonin, but blue-free white light using a violet chip LED prevents nocturnal melatonin suppression. (Copyright Circadian Light Research Center)

1. **Total Overnight Melatonin** production is suppressed by blue-rich light at night bright enough to cause circadian disruption.[180]

Suppressed levels of total overnight melatonin are strongly associated with an increased risk of breast cancer, prostate cancer, diabetes, hypertension, coronary artery disease, and depression , all of which are conditions that are exacerbated by the circadian disruption caused by blue-rich light at night.[181]

2. **Glucose Intolerance and Insulin Resistance** is increased by blue-rich light in the evening and overnight.[182] Increased glucose intolerance and insulin resistance are characteristic of pre-diabetes and Type 2 (adult onset) diabetics.

3. **Sleep Duration and Quality** are disrupted by insufficient blue-rich light during the day and/or excessive blue-rich light in the late evening. Sleep deprivation and fatigue are associated with reduced daytime alertness and impaired performance.[183]

SCIENTIFIC ASIDE:
Measuring the Biomarkers

Total Overnight Melatonin

In the absence of light, or under very dim light conditions, melatonin secretion from the pineal gland starts to rise about two hours before habitual bedtime (so-called Dim Light Melatonin Onset or DLMO). Melatonin levels in blood and saliva then climb to reach their peak levels around 2 am before falling to low levels around dawn. The total amount of melatonin produced overnight (e.g. from 8 pm to 8 am) can be measured as metabolites in first-morning urine, or by calculating the area under the curve from the blood or saliva melatonin measurements taken at intervals during the night.

Glucose Intolerance and Insulin Resistance

The glucose tolerance test is a standard diagnostic test for diabetes. It requires the person to fast overnight and have a blood sample taken before they are given a bottle of sugary water (containing glucose) to drink. Then, for the next two hours, blood samples are drawn at half-hourly intervals. When the insulin and glucose levels in those blood samples are measured in an average non-diabetic person, the fasting levels are low (glucose below *120 mg/dl*) and then rise before falling back to near normal levels after 2 hours. In a person with diabetes, or a healthy person exposed to blue-rich LED light overnight, the fasting levels are higher and do not return to normal levels within 2 hours.

Sleep and Alertness

Sleep duration and quality can be measured using portable devices such as wrist actigraphy, with or without sleep logs, or by EEG (electroencephalogram) polysomnography. Key measurements are: the time it takes to fall asleep after going to bed, the number of awakenings during the night, the total duration of sleep and, sleep efficiency (what

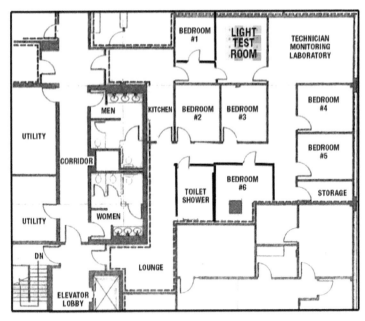

Floor plan of the Circadian Light Research Center where people can live, work, and sleep 24 hours a day under controlled daytime and nighttime lighting so that the effects of different types of lighting on human health can be studied. (Copyright Circadian Light Research Center)

percentage of the time was the person asleep between first falling asleep and their awakening in the morning.)

Circadian Light Research Center

To conduct these evaluations of the effects of lighting on health, we built in 2010 a Circadian Light Research Center located on Boston's Route 128 Hi Tech Corridor. In this research facility, exposure to light could be fully controlled. It has a light-controlled workplace simulation area, six individual lightproof bedrooms, bathroom, shower, kitchen and exercise area equipped so that volunteers can live and work in our facility for several days or a week.

With funding from the National Institutes of Health and other sources, volunteers were exposed to various types of lights in the Circadian Light Research Center and studied using a full range of physiological, psychological, performance, and medical tests, including:

- Sleep and wakefulness with continuous EEG monitoring

- Blood tests (e.g. lipids, cardiac disease markers)

- Glucose Tolerance tests and insulin resistance

- 24-hour urine melatonin collection

- Salivary Melatonin at 30-minute intervals

- Blood pressure

- Alertness & performance tests

- Mood and Depression scale tests

SCIENTIFIC ASIDE:
How Studies of Light and Health are Done

A pool of volunteers with a balanced distribution of age, sex, and ethnicity are recruited by advertising opportunities to be a paid research subject. They are given a complete description of the study so they can decide whether to give informed consent. Each volunteer is pre-screened for medical or psychiatric conditions which might influence the study results or create unacceptable risks. To protect the subjects, all protocols and consent forms are reviewed and approved by an Institutional Review Board registered for Federal Wide Assurance (FWA) with the Office for Human Research Protections (OHRP) of the Department of Health and Human Services (HHS).

For seven days before any study, all participants are instructed to maintain a preset sleep schedule at home and to maintain sleep diaries, which are confirmed using wrist actigraphs, a device the size of a wristwatch that measures motion and can distinguish whether a person is awake or asleep.

During every study, the timing and intensity of exposure to light, the timing of bed rest, and the content and timing of meals, and other activities are carefully controlled to ensure they are kept consistent between the tests of one light versus another.

In the controlled environment of the Circadian Light Research Center, we showed that there were substantial benefits to using blue-depleted lights during the evening and night hours as opposed to conventional blue-enriched LED lights.[184]

- **Total Overnight Melatonin** production was significantly increased under blue-depleted circadian night lights. With <2% blue lights at night over six times more melatonin was produced between 8:00 pm and 8:00 am compared to conventional blue-rich LED lights at the same illumination intensity. We can reasonably conclude that the multiple benefits of nocturnal melatonin in suppressing cancer cells, and supporting healthy metabolism and immunity are protected and enhanced by low blue lights at night.

- **Glucose Intolerance and Insulin Resistance** were prevented by blue-depleted lights. With nighttime exposure to conventional blue-rich LED lights, insulin resistance was doubled, rendering the healthy subjects into a pre-diabetic state. In contrast, blue-depleted circadian night lights prevented the pre-diabetic condition, even though both lights were at the same illumination intensity.

- **Increased Appetite** induced by blue-rich LED lights at night was reversed by the blue-depleted circadian night lights. This increased appetite leads to more snacking on the night shift and the excessive obesity too often seen in night or rotating shift workers.

- **Circadian Disruption** was prevented by blue-depleted lights. Conventional blue-enriched LED lights during an overnight study delay-shifted the peak of melatonin. This disruption in circadian timing was reversed by the blue-depleted LED lights at the same illumination intensity.

- **Vigilance Performance** was improved by the blue depleted violet pump circadian night lights. Conventional blue-pump LED lights increased vigilance performance, but not as much as the violet pump circadian night lights. And the circadian blue-depleted night lights improved performance without causing all the other undesirable effects of blue-enriched LED light at night.

In summary, these studies under carefully controlled conditions in the Circadian Light Research Center showed the multiple benefits of using spectrally-engineered circadian night lights, which prevent circadian disruption by light at night.

Real World Workplace Studies

The real test is how the circadian-optimized lights perform in the real world. To conduct these studies, we built a set of

Circadian lighting installation in the 24/7 operations center of an energy company. The lights automatically transition from daytime blue-rich to nocturnal blue-depleted light at local dawn and dusk across the seasons of the year according to the local latitude and longitude of the installation site. (Copyright Circadian Light Research Center)

standard ceiling light fixtures (called "troffers") which are seen in many offices. We fitted them with circadian day and night LEDs and internal day-night controls as described in Chapter 8: *Creating Healthy Light*.

To make these fixtures easy for an electrician to install, we developed an automatic control system inside each fixture with a ten-year clock that switched between day and night LEDs in sync with local sunset and sunrise, at whatever latitude and longitude the light fixtures were installed. It could be set according to zip code so that the circadian lights would automatically switch from day to night mode as the sun sets below the horizon throughout each year.

Since 2017, we have been installing these circadian fixtures in the 24/7 control rooms of Fortune 500 companies, and other

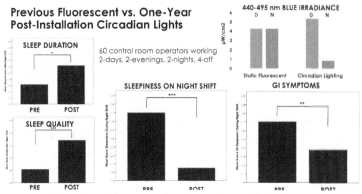

*Impact of circadian lighting with low blue nights and high blue days versus
conventional static fluorescent lights installed in the central control room of
the largest Dow Chemical plant in Europe at Terneuzen in the Netherlands.
(van Eekelen et al (2024))*

critical locations such as hospital intensive care patient rooms.
These circadian fixtures had already been scientifically validated
in the Circadian Light Research Center studies. It was now
time to see how they functioned in the real-world operations
of Chevron, Dow Chemical, Duke Energy, Georgia Pacific,
Siemens, National Grid, the U.S. Coastguard, and dozens of
other critical operations.

We got highly positive ratings from the employees working in these operations. We also collected data from year-long
studies comparing the circadian lighting with the previous
lighting in the facility.[185] These studies showed the installation
of circadian day-night lighting systems led to:

- Improved sleep duration and quality both before and
  after night shift

- 50% reduction in excessive sleepiness on the Epworth Scale

- 100% increase in alertness at 5 AM – the hardest time to
  stay awake on night shifts

- 45% reduction in the average number of snacks eaten during night shifts

- 20% reduction in employees with gastrointestinal disorders

- 67% Reduction in Control Room Operator Errors

- 43% Reduction in the use of Over-the-Counter (OTC) pain medications

Other Examples of Circadian Lighting Benefits

Over the last few years, there have been multiple other reports of health and performance benefits achieved by controlling the day-night timing of exposure to sky-blue wavelengths of light. Here are a few examples:

Nursing Homes for the Elderly

A major trial in four nursing homes in Wisconsin, with a total 758 residents, by researchers from Harvard Medical School, shows that installing circadian lighting substantially decreased the number of falls by elderly residents. Over a two-year study period, two of the nursing homes served as a control by keeping their conventional fluorescent lighting unchanged. After a control year the other two nursing homes had their common areas and resident bedrooms equipped with circadian lighting that provided blue-enriched white light from 6 am to 6 pm and blue-depleted white light from 6 pm to 6 am.

In the two nursing homes with circadian lighting, the number of falls was reduced from 297 to 173 per year, but the number of falls was unchanged in the two nursing homes that retained the conventional static lighting. In this large study of 126,479 resident days, with an elderly population with an average age of 81, 31% of whom had dementia, this translates as 4.82 falls/1000 resident days with circadian lighting vs. 8.44 falls/1000 resident days with conventional static fluorescent electric lighting.[186] The results remained significant after adjusting for age, sex, and dementia.

This is a huge benefit because falls are the leading cause of injury-related death in adults aged 65 years and over in the United States. A reduction of 126 elderly falls during the study period is a highly significant benefit, both for the well-being of the residents, and for the economics of running, and not having to recruit new residents for a nursing home.

Stroke Patients

The Stroke Unit at Rigshospitalet Glostrup in Denmark has been conducting research since 2013 on the effectiveness of circadian lighting by comparing stroke patients randomly assigned to either their N45 unit with conventional lighting or their N35 unit where the lighting is on a circadian program with blue-rich daytime lighting and blue-free lighting during evenings & nights. In a study of 90 stroke rehabilitation patients admitted for more than two weeks in 2014-2015, they found their patients in the N35 circadian lighting unit were 30 percent less fatigued and 49 percent less depressed, as compared to the patients from the neighboring ward N45, which had standard indoor lighting.[187]

Brain Trauma

In patients recovering from mild traumatic brain injury after suffering a concussion, early morning blue light exposure can aid the healing process. A randomized, double-blind, placebo-controlled trial of 32 adults by the University of Arizona

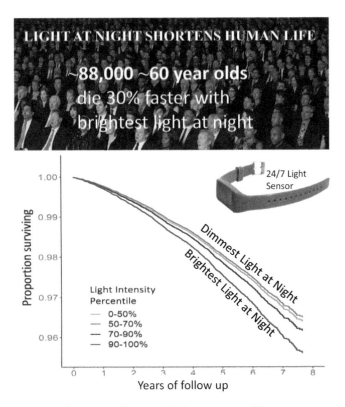

The impact of nocturnal light exposure on lifespan.
(Windred et al 2023)

showed that 6-weeks of daily 30-min pulses of blue light each morning improved sleep, reduced daytime sleepiness, and improved executive functioning, and was associated with an increased volume of the posterior thalamus, an area of the brain important for attention and visual processing.[188] These effects were not obtained in the patients randomly assigned to the placebo group and received similar treatments with amber color light instead of blue.

The Scale of the Opportunity

When Edison introduced electric lights in 1880, the average life expectancy in the USA was 39 years.[189] In the intervening years, major advances in medicine, biotechnology, and public health have doubled life expectancy. But this peaked at 79 years in 2014 and then, despite continued advances in medicine, plateaued between 2015 and 2019 before dropping to 76 years by 2021.[190] The COVID-19 epidemic certainly had an impact in 2020 and 2021. However, there are other significant contributors including opioid deaths, suicides and gun violence which are related to the increasing levels of mental health disorders in our society, including anxiety, depression and PTSD.

Largely overlooked in studies of human life expectancy has been the impact of circadian disruption induced by the wrong light at the wrong time. The breakthrough came with the UK BioBank study involving 88,000 people with an average age of 60, whose light exposure was tracked day and night and then who were followed for 6 years. Those who had the most light exposure at night had a dramatic decrease in life expectancy as compared to those who slept in the dark at night, dying 40% faster from cardiovascular disease and 30% faster from all causes of death.[191] There was also a large impact of daytime light exposure and nighttime lighting on psychiatric disorders. The quartile (25% of the participants) with the most nocturnal light exposure had 30% more Major Depressive Disorders, PTSD, Self-harm, and Psychosis, and those with the least light exposure during the day had a 20% increase in these psychiatric illnesses.[192]

Coincident with the plateauing of life expectancy has been the introduction of blue-rich light into American homes. In 2014, when life expectancy peaked, virtually everyone still used incandescent and halogen light bulbs in the evening with about 4% blue content. By 2016 15% of household bulbs had been replaced by LEDs with typically 14% blue content, and by 2018 33% of light bulbs were these blue-rich LEDs.[193]. In 2023, with the ban implemented on the sale of incandescent, and halogen light bulbs, more than 90% of lamps used in the evening in American home are blue-rich LEDs.

Replacing these conventional LEDs with circadian lighting that is free of sky-blue wavelengths in the evening would represent an enormous opportunity to reduce circadian disruption, and its associated disease burden of psychiatric, cardiovascular, and other health conditions, and enable the average lifespan to start climbing again.

In this chapter, you have learned:

1. Lights modulating blue content across day and night could qualify as safe medical devices, but it is better to treat them as General Wellness Devices.

2. There is considerable laboratory evidence showing that circadian-modulated lighting can restore melatonin and other circadian rhythms, reduce insulin resistance, prevent excess appetite and obesity and improve cognitive performance and mood.

3. Large-scale studies in the real world confirm the benefits of circadian lighting and show it can have significant positive impacts on health, lifespan, and human productivity.

PART 3:

LIGHTING

YOUR

OWN LIFE

10

Becoming a Smart Consumer of Light

How to find the light you need to consume in your daily light diet.

A Vision of the Future

In a few years, you will wake up in the morning to a gradually rising intensity of light rich in blue and green designed to stimulate the M-cones and ipRGC cells in your still dark-adapted eyes and gently blow away the sleepiness of the night. This spectral recipe jump-starts the readjustment of your circadian clock to its optimal relationship to natural dawn and dusk based on your individual "chronotype" – the genetically-determined attributes of your own circadian clock.[194] As you walk into the bathroom, the light transitions to a white light with perfect color rendering that both flatters your face in the mirror and delivers the dosage of circadian blue light required to stabilize your circadian clock. Once you have fully woken up and got the kids off to school, you take a morning walk or run outside to get a healthy dose of blue-rich, bright full spectrum natural daylight. If you cannot get outside that day because of the weather, infirmity, or pressing demands of the day, the spectral analyzer in your smartwatch, brooch, or eyeglasses detects this. It adjusts the indoor lights in each room you enter to ensure an enhanced morning dose of circadian blue light within the white spectrum lighting that enters your eyes.

You answer your emails and join a Zoom call to check in with a client and a Teams call with your office colleagues based in Los Angeles and Paris. You take a light lunch but find yourself getting sleepy, which will make it hard to complete the report you have to deliver to your boss later that afternoon. Ideally, you would take a short nap, but today, you are going to have to power through. So, you touch the button on your smartphone app which temporarily adjusts the spectral recipe for your lights and your computer screen to provide a 420 nm violet boost which stimulates your alertness, creativity, and productivity, and enables you to get the job done in time.

Your daughter was well enough to go to school today but had a few sniffles, so her bedroom lights during the day have been bathing the room in 405 nm violet light to kill the viruses on surfaces and stop further spread throughout the house. It's a winter evening, so the sun is setting as she arrives home from school, and the lights throughout the house switch to zero circadian blue mode, but the color is well balanced, so you barely notice the change. After dinner your daughter will need good quality light in her room to do her homework assignments. So the light is white but devoid of any circadian blue that would suppress her evening melatonin rise, or disrupt her sleep at bedtime. Her laptop screen and her mobile phone are equipped with a circadian-modulated color gamut that emits blue, green, and red during the day but automatically replaces them with circadian protective violet, green and red in the evening hours – a change that is "metameric" - barely perceptible to the human eye. Fortunately, the laptop and mobile screen makers have abandoned their NightShift® & BlueShade® color-tuning placebos which yellowed screens in the evening without removing the critical sleep-disrupting blue. Instead, it is the violet wavelengths emitted from the screens and bedroom lights that temporarily stimulate her alertness and creativity as long as she needs it. The lights then switch to orange-red when she needs to wind down, which enables her to fall asleep quickly once she switches off the lights. If she should fall asleep with the lights on, sensors automatically detect that she is asleep and turn all lights off to ensure she sleeps in the dark.

Later that evening, your spouse arrives back from a business trip to Tokyo. He ensured he stayed in a hotel room equipped with circadian lighting that minimized the disruption of his circadian clock by controlling the circadian blue content of light to match his chronotype, circadian timing, and travel schedule. On the airplane coming back he booked a seat in the section designed for travelers needing to reset to the US Eastern time zone. His spectral analyzer had recorded his circadian blue light exposure throughout his trip and adjusted the lights once he reached home to help him stably resynchronize to local home time. Because he is concerned about his developing bald spot, he also gets 640 nm red wavelengths, which boost hair growth, added to the light emitted from the fixtures and bulbs above his head.

Your mother is staying with you while your husband is away. She has some mild cognitive impairment and has been prescribed a 40 Hz light and sound treatment for an hour each day. It used to be done with goggles, but now it can be delivered by the lights in her bedroom by using metameric lighting, where the light spectrum changes 40 times a second but looks the same to the eye. She also suffers from migraines, and when these happen the lights can deliver green-rich light which helps relieve the pain.

What You Can Do Today

This is an exciting time for healthy lighting. Automated lighting systems are starting to emerge that provide some of the circadian spectral recipes required to optimize human-light interactions across day and night. But there is no one-stop-shop or single supplier of all the lamps and fixtures you need. So, for the time being, you will need to be a smart consumer to ensure you and your family get the full benefits of circadian lighting.

The first-generation smart lights, like Phillips Hue, allowed you to select and program a broad range of colors and correlated color temperatures (CCT), but did not provide evidence-based circadian spectral recipes.[195] They were smart and pretty, but ineffective at protecting your health. They can light your room in any color you could imagine, but this is for your entertainment, not your health.

Second-generation smart circadian light bulbs and fixtures are now coming onto the market that offer the validated spectral recipes required for healthy day, evening and night lighting. They are not yet fully integrated, but you cannot afford to wait, as the health and well-being of you and your family are at stake. So, in this chapter, I will help you find the lighting products that are currently available to promote your health, improve your sleep, and minimize the harm of light exposure in the evening after the sun has set below the horizon. It is a fast-developing area so you should follow my posts on Substack and consult my website https://circadianlight.org for the latest updates.

Do Not Let Your Electrician be Your Doctor

Buying lights in a big box store can be overwhelming. You are confronted by row upon row of lighting products, virtually all containing royal blue pump LEDs. Going into your local hardware store is not much better in terms of lighting product offerings, although you will often get better service and advice. Even consulting an electrician on which lights to install won't solve the problem. Getting advice from the guy in the hardware store or an electrician who doesn't understand healthy circadian lighting is useless and may be ill-advised. They only know how to focus on color, energy efficiency, and cost.

So, my tip of the day is "Do not let your electrician or hardware store clerk be your doctor". That is your responsibility. You must know the specs of healthy circadian lighting, and make sure they give you bulbs and fixtures that meet those specs.

When choosing lights, you need to consider not only illumination quality and energy efficiency, but also health and wellness, alertness, creativity, and productivity. That way, you can ensure you are protecting your health and well-being, and living your best self.

Your Light Diet

The light you see is as essential for your health as the food you eat, the water you drink and the air you breathe. You should be as thoughtful about your light diet as you are about your nutritional diet and know the different spectral recipes your eyes need to see at various times throughout the 24-hour day.

To keep your body properly in sync with the Earth's rotation, you need to be exposed to specific spectral recipes at different times of day. As with food, you have light dietary choices and sensitivities, and some light diets are more suited to some people than others.

So much is written on nutritional diets, but virtually nothing on light diets. For example, the world's largest book publisher, Penguin Random House, lists a staggering 1,940 books on nutritional diets, but has published only one book on the equally important subject of light and health, and that was back in 2013 before LED lights even hit the market.[196] Now 1,940 books are a lot of books. If you stacked them on top of each other, the pile would reach over 160 feet high.

The healthiest natural light diet was re-created in the camping trips without electricity in the wilds of Colorado that we discussed in Chapter 2: *Goodbye Milky Way*. Sleeping in the

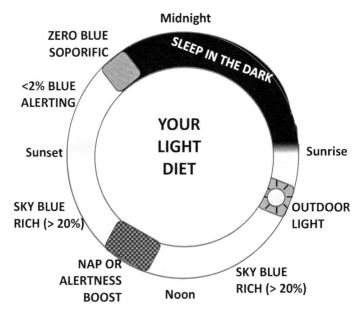

Basic elements of a light diet at the spring and fall equinoxes. The timing of the various spectral recipes will vary with your individual chronotype and the seasons of the year. (Copyright Circadian Light Research Center)

dark at night, being awakened by the rising sun in the mornings, and remaining outdoors all day, before spending your evenings illuminated by wood firelight devoid of blue. But in today's world, we have to compromise. Our jobs and duties often require us to be indoors 90% or more of the time. Under these conditions, adhering to a healthy light diet is vital.

Light diets must be individualized because our circadian systems are genetically determined. Just like the Myers-Briggs personality test, there are four parameters.[197]

1. Lark vs. Owl: Early morning riser vs. late night type.

2. Flexible Sleeper vs. Rigid Sleeper: Can sleep at any time vs. only able to sleep on a set schedule.

3. Consolidated Sleeper vs. Napper: Can only obtain sleep at night vs. able to nap during the day.

4. Short Sleeper vs. Long Sleeper: Fully refreshed with less than 7 hours sleep vs. needing 9 hours or more.

Everyone falls somewhere on each scale, with most of us in the middle of the range. So, to keep it simple for now, let's follow a light diet over a day for the average person spending 90% of their time indoors.

Sleeping in the Dark

Sleeping in a dark room at night is critical for your health to enable your body's repair and immune processes to be fully effective. If you need a clock in the bedroom, make sure the dial is dim red light, and use dim orange or red lights near the floor to prevent trips and falls on the way to the bathroom. To make sure you don't wake up too early in the morning during summer months, use dark drapes or lightproof shutters.

Morning Light

Since you will be fully dark-adapted when you awake, you will need time to gradually adapt to light in the morning. So, keeping the lights relatively dim is OK for the first 5-10 minutes. But after that, you need to be exposed to light rich in sky-blue wavelengths. Getting outside for a walk before the sun is high in the sky for 30-60 minutes is ideal for synchronizing your circadian clocks and starting the day right. The rest of the morning, whether you get outside or not, sit close to a large window or make sure you are bathed in >20% sky blue light. You may need to use a supplemental blue light source to achieve the blue dosage required.

Post-Lunch

It is natural for your energy and mental sharpness to slip in the early afternoon - the so called "post-lunch dip", although it occurs whether you eat lunch or not. If your chronotype makes you a "Napper" and you have somewhere to do it, a brief nap - no more than 45 minutes - can give you a new boost to the day. Alternatively, a dose of blue or violet short-wavelength light can restore your alertness even more effectively than a caffeinated drink, and improve your sleep at night.

Early Evening

Sky-blue light must be removed from your light diet once the sun sets outside. You can do this with very low Kelvin (<1800K) orange light, but this can make it hard to do any detailed task or productive work or stay awake until bedtime. Better in the early evening is zero blue light with a violet pump which can provide an attractive light that should keep you in a good mood and enable you to read, and stay awake.

Late Evening

To help you wind down and get ready for bed, orange-red light with no blue or violet content can be very effective.

The Four Dimensions of Lighting

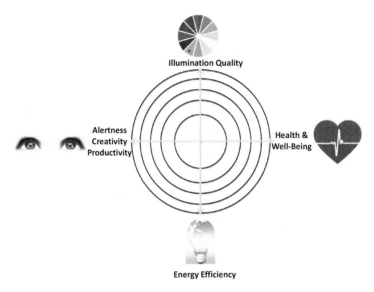

The four dimensions of lighting need to be balanced.
(Copyright Circadian Light Research Center)

When evaluating the lighting choices (i.e. the spectral recipes) for your light diet, as we discussed in Chapter 8: *Creating Healthy Light,* you need to balance all four priorities of lighting:

1. **Illumination Quality:** Light that provides adequate visual discrimination to accomplish your tasks and provides accurate color rendering so that objects look similar to how they would under natural light.

2. **Health and Wellness:** Maintaining the synchrony and harmony of your body with the natural day-night cycle is

vital for your health. We need lights that are rich in circadian sky-blue wavelengths during the day and depleted of them at night.

3. **Alertness, Creativity, and Productivity:** Light that contains short wavelengths (violet and blue) stimulates alertness and boosts creative thinking and productivity. Even more effective than a cup of coffee, these effects are rapid onset, and after the short wavelength light is switched off are short-lasting, so subsequent sleep is not disrupted.

4. **Energy Efficiency:** Historically measured in lumens per watt, energy efficiency was defined as the amount of visual (photopic) illumination per watt of energy. But we need better metrics because lumens/watt fails to measure how energy efficient is a light at delivering health and wellness, or for stimulating alertness, creativity and productivity.

So, let's now look at how various types of lighting match up.

Incandescent Bulbs

Most modern lighting fails miserably at meeting these balanced objectives. Even the incandescent light bulbs that were Edison's

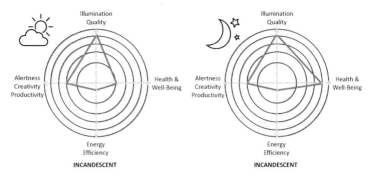

Assessing incandescent light bulbs across the four dimensions of lighting for day and night use. (Copyright Circadian Light Research Center)

legacy, only met some of the priorities. Incandescent lights provide good illumination quality but are low in lumens per watt efficiency. Ninety percent of the electricity they consume is turned into infrared heat. Incandescent light bulbs also emit about 4% circadian blue, which provides little benefit in synchronizing your circadian rhythms during the daytime at normal indoor light levels, nor in stimulating alertness and productivity. However, provided the incandescent lighting is not too bright, it can be relatively healthy when used in the evening and at night– in other words, it will not cause much circadian clock disruption.

That's why I stocked up with an ample supply of incandescent light bulbs in my basement when the initial bans on 40- and 60-watt incandescent light bulbs were announced on January 1st, 2014, as part of the efficiency standards signed into law by President George W. Bush in 2007.[198] That has enabled me to avoid putting any blue pump LED light bulbs in my house, while I got to work on inventing safe and healthy circadian lighting alternatives with my team at the Circadian Light Research Center.

Royal Blue Pump LED Lighting

2014 saw the start of the widespread adoption of LED light

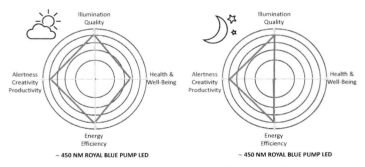

Assessing blue-chip LED lights across the four dimensions of lighting for day and night use. (Copyright Circadian Light Research Center)

bulbs and fixtures, driven by these energy policies. These first-generation LEDs with an approximately 450 nm royal blue pump addressed energy efficiency by providing a twenty-fold increase in lumens of light produced per watt of electricity.

Many, but not all, royal blue pump LEDs produce reasonable quality illumination. They also provide blue wavelengths that can stimulate alertness and help synchronize circadian clocks during the day. However, the blue light emitted by these LEDs is relatively low in the 460- 495 nm wavelengths which maximize health during the day. They typically use an LED chip with peak emission at about 450 nm to maximize the lumens per watt efficiency, and the amount of blue they emit is relatively lower at the circadian peak sensitivity of 480 nm.

It is quite a different matter at night. The blue light these LEDs produce after sunset suppresses melatonin and shifts the timing of circadian clocks, causing circadian disruption and ill health. They typically emit 10 to 15% blue light in the 440 – 495 nm range, depending on their color temperature (CCT) compared to only 4% blue emitted by incandescent bulbs.

The irony is to save the health of the planet, the Department of Energy promotes LED lighting that harms human health. Fortunately, as discussed in *Chapter 8: Creating Healthy Light*, it is now possible to use the power of LED spectral engineering to create energy-efficient lights that also promote circadian harmony and good health.

Spectrally Engineered Day and Night Circadian LEDs

The secret is, of course, to control the blue content of light across day and night. As you know by now the formula is light rich in approximately 480 nm blue during daylight hours, and light depleted of blue after sunset. These LED lights ap-

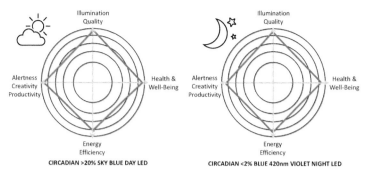

Assessing spectrally-engineered LED lights across the four dimensions of lighting for day and night use. (Copyright Circadian Light Research Center)

propriately balance illumination quality, energy efficiency, health and well-being and alertness and productivity. During the day the blue wavelengths synchronize the circadian clock and boost alertness and productivity. At night, alertness is maintained by short wavelength violet light, and the absence of blue ensures the avoidance of circadian disruption.

1800K Night LED

Another approach to blue-free nocturnal lighting is to reduce the correlated color temperature (CCT) below 1800K, or to use only orange and red LEDs. In many ways, this light mimics the wood fires of pre-electric days and has minimal disruptive effects on circadian clocks because the light is essentially devoid of sky-blue light.

However, there is a trade-off. The quality of the illumination is reduced, and visual acuity - such as the ability to

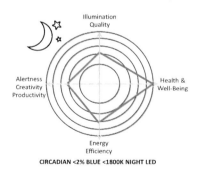

Assessing an 1800K LED light across the four dimensions of lighting for evening use. (Copyright Circadian Light Research Center)

read - is compromised. Furthermore, this orange color light reduces alertness and can depress mood. It is not the light to use if you want to accomplish meaningful work, but it is a good solution for the last 30-60 minutes of the day before going to sleep.

Lighting Your Home Around the Clock

Ideally, the lights in your home should dynamically adjust the spectral recipes in your light diet according to the time of day. The challenge is that many circadian lighting products available today are static – in other words, they do not change their spectrum by time of day. So, you have to choose different lights in different rooms in your house depending on the time of day you occupy them.

But that is all changing. Dynamic circadian lighting is now being introduced to the market – as described in the *Resources* section. Linear architectural "Circadian Blue" lighting fix-

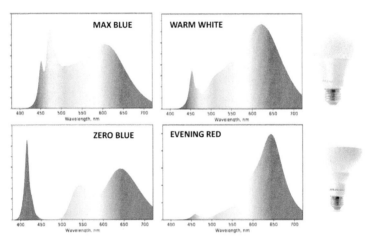

Soraa 4-channel connected light bulbs (A-19 & BR-30) cycling between Max-Blue to sync the circadian clock, museum quality warm white, ZeroBlue to enable safe and productive evenings, and late evening red to prepare for sleep. (Courtesy of Korrus)

tures. from the Lumium division of Korrus automatically cycle between Max Blue day and Zero Blue night spectral recipes.

In addition, the Soraa division of Korrus offers Zero Blue light bulbs, and has developed A-19 and BR-30 light bulbs that automatically cycle through four spectral recipes depending on the time of day. There is a MaxBlue spectrum, which delivers the >20% sky-blue light at the times required to sync the circadian clock, a museum blue-rich quality light for regular daytime use, a white zero blue light with violet for enhanced alertness in the early evening, and a 1400K orange light for winding down before going to sleep.

Spectrasol Sunflow floor lamp with ceiling solar spectrum blue rich light for daytime, wall warm white and blue-free firelight at floor level to protect circadian health and sleep at night. (Courtesy of Spectrasol)

At the same time, Spectrasol is releasing a Sunflow floor lamp for the European market, which cycles between an overhead daytime solar light spectrum rich in blue, a warm white light at wall level and a firelight-color light at your feet for the evening.[199] Other manufacturers, including Osin's Loop and Bios' Skyview, offer lamps that provide supplemental sky-blue light during the day to enhance conventional lighting when it does not provide enough blue, and then automatically cycle to blue-free light in the evening.[200] In addition, multiple manufacturers offer static high CCT lights for the daytime (which have to be at least 6500K to be effective) and low CCT lights for the evening (which have to be less than 1800K to remove sufficient blue).

Another source of uncontrolled blue light is the screens we use. Americans spend 7 hours a day, Brits 6 hours and South Africans 9 hours in front of screens.[201] But we no longer have to use screens that pollute our evenings with blue light. Korrus has developed white computer screens automatically and imperceptibly switching between 20% sky blue light during the day and less than 2% at night.[202]

So, the tools are now becoming available to provide a safe and healthy light diet for our homes. Chapter 11: *When You Don't Control the Space* discusses what you can do about the harmful or inadequate light to which you are exposed outside your home.

In this chapter, you have learned:

1. In the future, lighting will automatically adjust spectral recipe and intensity across your day to promote health and well-being. but you shouldn't wait because many of the benefits can be obtained from lights available today.

2. You need to replace conventional lighting that only provides illumination, and lumens/watt efficiency, with spectrally-engineered circadian lights that protect your health and well-being and boost your alertness and productivity.

3. Light bulbs and fixtures are entering the market that enable you to automatically control your daily light diet in your home.

11

When You Don't Control the Space

**How to demand healthy lighting
in spaces you don't control.**

When you leave your home and enter any other building, you are exposed to lighting that you didn't choose, which has unknown effects on your health and well-being. It is not easy to tell by looking at the lights in a building how much blue light is reaching your eyes and whether it is too little for daytime or too much after sunset.

If you are dropping by the post office to mail a parcel, or a florist to get some flowers, the few minutes you spend there will have little consequence. But if you are going to spend multiple hours in your workplace, a school, or multiple days in a hotel or hospital, you should care about the lights to which you are exposed. Or if you happen to work in that post office or flower shop, you should be concerned.

You have the right to ask that every indoor space, where you or your family spend significant time, delivers blue-rich light in the daytime hours and blue-depleted light after dark. Whether you are working in a factory, hospital, call center, or Amazon warehouse, or trading equities at a Wall Street desk, exposure to conventional blue-rich LED and fluorescent light in the evening hours and at night significantly increases your risk of obesity, diabetes and heart disease, as well as certain cancers. If your elderly parent is in a nursing home, you should also care about the lighting. With properly designed circadian lighting, sleep disturbances can be cut in half, agitation in the residents reduced by 70%, and the risk of falls reduced by 43%.[203]

Round-the-clock exposure to bright blue-rich LED, and fluorescent lights are a significant and unnecessary health hazard for hospital patients and staff. (iStock/com/VlLevi)

Do No Harm

If you are a young nurse or doctor working overnight shifts in a hospital or nursing home, you should worry about your exposure to blue rich fluorescent and LED lights that are associated with substantially greater breast cancer risk in women and prostate cancer risk in men. But you should also be very concerned about the impact of round-the-clock blue-rich light on your patients. Doing no harm is a fundamental principle of medicine, and while not actually part of the Hippocratic Oath, it was first promulgated in 400 BC by Hippocrates in *Of The Epidemics*.[204] Unfortunately, it is now clear that standard hospital lighting is doing much unnecessary harm to the patients under their care.

As Ralph Booth, inventor of the OSIN Loop, tells:

> "What drove me to try to elicit change in the lighting industry was my wife getting leukemia 11 years ago. She ended up for weeks on end in isolation rooms before and after her stem cell transplant. I knew even back then that the artificial light in Ellen's room was doing nothing to align her circadian rhythms. I also knew that we were planning a brand-new hospital, and with the knowledge that was known and plain to understand, I naively thought that the critical areas of the new Christchurch Hospital would have lighting that is spectrally tuned to ensure better long term patient outcomes. 11 years on I am sad to say that the isolation rooms have LED lighting that is not spectrally tuned. This got me so frustrated I decided to do something about it, I started OSIN and developed the Loop, a lamp for biological light".

How hard it is to do anything about it was illustrated by my experience proposing circadian lighting to the President of a Harvard teaching hospital. We had developed circadian lighting that automatically switched from blue-rich day to blue-depleted night with little change in color temperature. Furthermore, we had installed them with very positive results in other safety-critical 24-hour operations such as Chevron and Dow Chemical. Naturally, we thought that hospitals would be the obvious next target.

Unfortunately, we found that the 130-bed, state-of-the-art facility, had just replaced all its lighting with LED fixtures shining blue-rich light around the clock. As a result, the hospital had been awarded certification as a LEED Gold® certified facility partly because of the improved lumens per watt electrical efficiency. It was a point of environmentally conscious pride trumpeted by their marketing department. To the hospital's credit, their architectural design did maximize daylight access to the building, but then they had undermined the benefits by using blue-rich LED light at night. However, they were just not willing at that time to replace the award-winning LEDs they had just installed.

In that case, our timing was off. But we have since been able to install circadian lighting in hospitals. When hospital rooms are equipped with lights that remove blue at night, melatonin levels are restored, and sleep is stabilized and improved, all of which help the healing process. For example, Chromaviso has installed circadian lighting in 40 hospitals and 60 senior living homes in Scandinavia. The impact of alternating between blue-rich daytime light and light with no blue content at night has been dramatic. It has reduced the length of hospital stays, and enabled a rapid and significant reduction in manic symptoms in bipolar patients, and decreased in depression in stroke patients.[205] It also has resulted in a 20% reduction in staff turnover.[206]

But despite all these benefits, circadian lighting still comprises less than 0.2% of the lighting market. The traditional way that lights are sold based on aesthetics, lumens

per watt efficiency and cost impedes adoption of this vital
new technology. So, it is up to the user and beneficiary –
that means you – to learn how to demand circadian lighting
in all the places where you spend your time.

How to Get Circadian Lighting Installed

Start by campaigning to get circadian lighting installed where
you and your family members spend the most time. To succeed,
you must understand how lighting decisions and purchases
are made. So, let me share what I have learned over the past
ten years about persuading building owners and occupants
to install evidence-based circadian lighting, and reap the very
real benefits.

Virtually all conventional (non-circadian) lighting sold
today is based on the same fundamental technology – the
static approximately 450 nm royal blue-chip LED. Lighting
has, as a result, become a commodity with the only differ-
entiation being aesthetics, lumens per watt efficiency and
cost. However, it is not only objective factors that are at play.
Lighting has traditionally been sold through a complex set
of carefully nurtured relationships between manufacturers,
sales representative agencies, distributors, architects, lighting
designers, lighting contractors and building facility managers. Dinners, golf outings and sports tickets foster loyalty,
so it is often more about who you know than what you sell.
It can be quite opaque, so most lighting manufacturers have
little idea who is buying their lights.

The typical buyer of commercial and public building lighting
is often not motivated to consider the health and well-being
of the building occupants. The performance and bonuses of
the building facility manager, and the profits of the building
owner, are based on how cheaply they can purchase lighting

and how much the lighting will reduce the electrical utility bill. The people most affected by the inadequate or harmful LED lighting – the building occupants, and the managers responsible for their performance, health and morale – are rarely consulted on which lights to purchase.

Even if the building occupants ask for "circadian lighting", there is no guarantee that evidence-based circadian lighting will be purchased. Most often what you will get is a color-tuning placebo. So, this is why you need to be knowledgeable and smart in your campaign for healthy circadian lighting.

Elements of a Successful Campaign: 1. Education

Most people are entirely unaware of the impact of lighting on health, so you need to start with education. The key to education is the WIIFM – What's in it For Me? And that, of course, depends on whom you are talking to.

Building Owner/Landlord: A building owner has no direct interest in the health of the building occupants. Instead, you need to convince the owner that installing circadian lighting could attract reliable tenants willing to pay premium rents. The WIIFM is the opportunity to add a few extra dollars per square foot for leases with circadian lighting because that can have a considerable compound effect on the building's value.

Business Owner/Senior Management: The health of employees affects a business's bottom line through its impact on their productivity, the rate of sickness/absenteeism, and the employee turnover rate. These can total over $30,000 per employee per year.[207] Hence, the WIIFM is the impact of circadian lighting in boosting employee performance, morale, and health.

Employee Occupants: Here, the WIIFM is more immediate. You need to explain that circadian lighting improves sleep quality, and reduces fatigue and malaise caused by circadian disruption. People are also concerned about their long-term health and lifespan, but that is often more distant and abstract, especially when they are young.

Elements of a Successful Campaign: 2. Know the Pros & Cons of Alternative Solutions

In Chapter 8: *Creating Healthy Light*, we discussed different ways of providing effective circadian lighting that delivers the correct amount of circadian sky-blue light (440-495 nm) entering the eyes of the people in the room during day and night. This corneal blue irradiance measured in $\mu W/cm^2$ determines the physiological responses and the health effects of that light, depending on the time of day. As discussed in Chapter 7: *Tuning to the Right Wavelength*, the minimum required daytime dosage is > 20 $\mu W/cm^2$, and the safe dosage after sunset is < 2 $\mu W/cm^2$.

So that you can know what these options look like and understand their pros and cons, we built a Circadian Light Demo, which shows three different ways to deliver the required minimum daytime dose of 20 $\mu W/cm^2$ 440-495 nm blue, and the maximum evening dosage of 2 $\mu W/cm^2$.

The circadian lights on the top row use spectral engineering to minimize the color and CCT change between day and night without changing the lux brightness of the light. The color-tuning approach in the middle row requires large Correlated Color Temperature (CCT) changes from 6500K to 1800K to provide the same circadian effect. This means a harsh bluish-white light during the day and a yellow-orange light in the evening. The third alternative, shown at the bot-

DAY (440-495nm) NIGHT
20 µW/cm²   2 µW/cm²

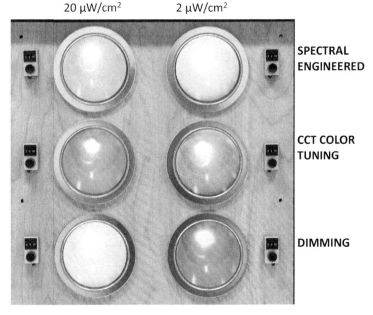

SPECTRAL
ENGINEERED

CCT COLOR
TUNING

DIMMING

Circadian lighting demo which provides the required dosages of circadian blue light. Top Left: circadian 480 nm peak day 4000K, Top Right: circadian zero blue night 3300K. Middle Left: Color-tuning 6500K Middle Right: 1800K. Bottom Left: 4000K 450nm LED at double lux brightness. Bottom Right: 4000K 450 nm LED dimmed tenfold. (Copyright Circadian Light Research Center)

tom, is to significantly brighten a conventional 4000K royal blue 450 nm peak LED light to provide sufficient blue during the day, and dim it ten-fold in the evening, both of which conditions can impair visual acuity and comfort. It is also possible, within limits, to combine brightening and dimming with the spectrally-engineered and CCT color-tuning options, provided acceptable levels of visual acuity and comfort are maintained, and the correct doses of circadian blue content are delivered.

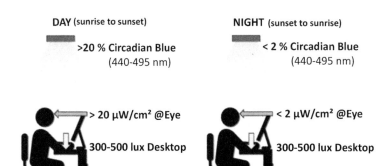

DAY (sunrise to sunset)	NIGHT (sunset to sunrise)
>20 % Circadian Blue (440-495 nm)	< 2 % Circadian Blue (440-495 nm)
> 20 µW/cm² @Eye	< 2 µW/cm² @Eye
300-500 lux Desktop	300-500 lux Desktop

Specifications for desktop visual illumination and for eye-level circadian efficacy (Copyright Circadian Light Research Center)

Elements of a Successful Campaign: 3. Spec Locks

The facilities manager, or the lighting contractor hired by the building owner, typically makes lighting decisions in an existing commercial or public building. They are not motivated to spend money on lighting. So, even if you insist on circadian lighting, they will look for the cheapest option their suppliers label "circadian lighting" whether it is effective or a placebo.

The answer is to know the "spec locks" that guarantee you will get effective circadian lighting, and to understand the types of lighting that will meet those spec locks.

Different metrics are required to define the visual illumination of a room versus the circadian health effects on the room occupants.

Visual Illumination

1. **Desktop Lux:** Most indoor lighting standards are based on desktop or tabletop illumination, also called horizontal illumination. For most workplaces the IES recommends 300 – 500 lux desktop illumination.[208] As

discussed in Chapter 8: *Creating Healthy Light*, lux and lumens are measures of visual brightness largely determined by green and yellow wavelengths, with very little input from blue or red.

2. **Lumens of Light Source**: The specification of light fixtures required to meet the desktop illumination standard is based on the lumens they produce, the percentage dimming of the light, and the distance of the light fixture from the desktop (remember the inverse square law of light we discussed in Chapter 6: *Bringing the Outside Indoors*).

Neither of these metrics defines the circadian properties of a light.

Spec Locks for Circadian Lights

When ordering circadian light bulbs and light fixtures that avoid the need for excessive brightening during the day and dimming at night, here are two convenient spec locks.

1. **Percent Blue of Light Source**: The simplest way to specify circadian light sources is based on the percentage of energy emitted by 440-495 nm wavelengths compared to all visible light wavelengths (380 – 780 nm). This can be calculated using an Excel spreadsheet from the spectral power distribution (SPD) of the light, which any manufacturer should be able to supply. As a rule of thumb with IES recommended 300 – 500 lux desktop illumination levels, you should look for light sources that emit < 2% 440-495 nm blue at night and >20% blue during the day. This will provide the physiologically required levels of eye-level sky-blue irradiance, and a spec lock that your lighting supplier cannot easily circumvent with placebo lighting.

2. **Blumens of Light Source**: Blumens are a robust new way to specify light sources for circadian lighting, that parallels the Lumens green-yellow metric for visual illumination. Blumens can be defined as the µW/cm2 440-495nm blue light emitted per 1000 lumens. This is conveniently scaled for lighting designers who specify light sources by lumens. A conventional 4000K 450nm royal blue LED light delivers about 40 Blumens. In comparison, an effective spectrally engineered circadian light delivers about 7 Blumens at night and 75 Blumens during the day, enabling circadian lighting without the requirement for dimming at night.

SCIENTIFIC ASIDE:
Other Circadian Lighting Metrics

Those who read the circadian lighting technical literature will find other metrics used by different groups of researchers and lighting specifiers.

Melanopic Equivalent Daylight Illuminance ("Melanopic EDI")

As we discussed in Chapter 7: *Tuning to the Right Wavelength*, the melanopsin photopigment in the ipRGC cells in the eye detecting the blue light that synchronizes circadian clocks has a peak sensitivity at 479 nm. The Melanopic EDI metric was derived by right-shifting the sensitivity curve by 11 nm to peak at 490nm aqua blue as a theoretical correction for the yellowing effect of the lens in the eye.[209] This results in a metric that is sensitive to green light as well as blue.

However, empirical evidence suggests this 11 nm correction does not apply to the normally light-adapted human eye. Studies in fully light-adapted people show the circadian peak sensitivity is at 480 +/- 3nm, and any green light effects fade away in the first 2 hours of light after leaving darkness.[210]

Currently, Melanopic EDI is adopted by standards groups such as the CIE (International Commission on Illumination) and Delos WELL.[211] The recommended daytime light level is a minimum of 250 melanopic EDI lux at the eye. During the evening, starting at least 3 hours before bedtime, the recommended maximum is 10 melanopic EDI lux, and for the sleep environment the recommended maximum is 1 melanopic EDI lux measured at the eye. It can be confusing because melanopic EDI lux is substantially different (about half of) the photopic lux brightness of a typical light.

Circadian Stimulus (CS)

Another metric used by some scientists, and adopted by UL (Underwriters Laboratory, UL DG 24480) is the Circadian Stimulus (CS) metric derived from the original dark-adapted eye data.[212] It is based on a complex model of the eye and has some fundamental flaws. For example, radically different values are obtained for lights with CCT values below about 3400K compared to above 3400K. This results in zero blue light below 3400K being classified as more circadian stimulatory than blue-rich light above 3400K, which is the exact opposite of the scientific evidence. Furthermore, we

> found no correlation whatsoever (R2 = 0.001) between
> the Circadian Stimulus (CS) values as described in UL
> DG 24480, and the overnight human melatonin data
> from people under normal workplace lighting conditions.

Neither of these metrics provides a simple and convenient way to specify circadian light bulbs and fixtures for day and night use, since they provide metrics for eye-level light and not for the light source itself. But they are used widely, and you should be aware of them.

Elements of a Successful Campaign: 4. Applying the Pressure

Armed with the WIIFM education strategy, and the spec locks to ensure you request effective lighting, you are now positioned to make the case for circadian lighting. Like any campaign, careful planning, research, and persuasive communication is required. You will have to identify key stakeholders who need to be convinced, identify potential allies, and gather support from other users of the space, (for example, your co-workers at your workplace, other parents at a school, or other users at a public library).

You must know the right ask. The International Dark Sky Association mistakenly campaigned for streetlights with less than 3000K CCT, believing that it would reduce the light pollution of our skies and the environment. This was based on a 2016 American Medical Association (AMA) policy statement about the impact of blue-rich light at night.[213] As I will discuss in Chapter 12: *Light Pollution and Biodiversity*, they were very effective in gaining public support and putting pressure on cities such as Chicago and Los Angeles to change their streetlights. However, using CCT as the standard was the wrong ask as it is only weakly related to blue content.

Political Action

Another approach is to campaign for a local ordinance or state law that bans harmful blue-rich light at night. Concerned with the effects of blue-rich LED lights on wildlife, the Hawaiian island of Maui in 2023 introduced a new ordinance #5434 which states that *"All outdoor lighting fixtures, except for neon, must limit short wavelength content to no more than 2 percent of blue light content. "Blue light content" means the ratio of the amount of energy emitted by the outdoor light fixture between 400 and 500 nm divided by the amount of energy between 400 nm and 700 nm"*.[214] Fines could reach $1,000 a day. In response, the major LED manufacturer Lumileds has developed Nightscape LED technology, which can meet the Maui standard.[215]

Outdoor lighting ordinances with the same intent have been passed elsewhere, and momentum is growing. However, some, like the one on Nantucket Island need to be better informed because they make the error of requiring outdoor lights to be 2700K CCT or less.[216]

Now, it is time to turn our attention to replacing indoor lighting that is insufficiently rich in blue during the day and too rich in blue at night. It is good to be concerned about wildlife, but even more important to be concerned about the harmful effects of LED lights on our families and loved ones.

Tangled Up in Blue

The predominant theme of Bob Dylan's song "Tangled Up in Blue" is trying to escape the recent past.[217] And that is what we are trying to do in a world indiscriminately lit with blue-rich fluorescent and LED light. But a $2.5 trillion installed base of lighting will have to be replaced – and that will take some time.

If you cannot change the lights because you don't own the

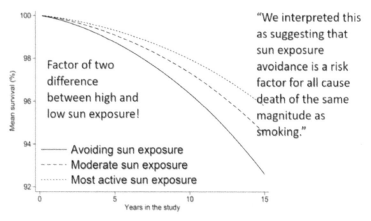

Mortality with Respect to Sun Exposure in Sweden [Lindqvist, 2016]

Factor of two difference between high and low sun exposure!

"We interpreted this as suggesting that sun exposure avoidance is a risk factor for all cause death of the same magnitude as smoking."

—— Avoiding sun exposure
- - - - Moderate sun exposure
·········· Most active sun exposure

The risk of staying indoors and avoiding sun exposure is as great as the risk for smoking. (Adapted from Lindqvist et al (2014))

building or cannot influence the owner, there are still things you can do to protect your health.

Using devices to add supplemental sky-blue light during the day, and to filter out the blue wavelengths of light from screens and lamps in the evening hours makes a lot of sense. The problem is that this is rarely done effectively, and there are too many irresponsible marketing claims unsupported by scientific evidence. So, let's look at the best practices.

Supplemental Daytime Blue

The ideal way to get the daytime blue light you need for synchronizing your circadian clocks and promoting good health is to get outside in natural daylight each day. People who see more sunlight each day live longer. A study of 29,518 Swedish women aged 25-64 years followed prospectively for 20 years showed that sunlight exposure greatly reduced deaths from cardiovascular disease and other non-cancer illnesses, such as diabetes, more than offsetting any increased risk from skin cancers.[218] Remarkably, the increased risk from staying indoors and avoiding sunlight was as large as the risk from smoking.

If you cannot get outside, and cannot easily change your inadequate indoor lighting, there are still practical options to provide the blue light you need for daytime health. Desktop lamps such as the Osin Loop, and Bios Skyview, and floor lamps such as the Spectrasol Sunflow provide sufficient daytime sky-blue light to protect circadian health.[219] These lamps automatically switch to blue-free light in the evenings based on your local time zone to protect you from circadian disruption. Another option is glass frames equipped with blue LEDS that fit over or replace your eyewear. For example, Re-Timer glasses are effective in delaying or advancing circadian melatonin and sleep, depending on whether you use them in the evening or morning.[220] The problem is that when used unwisely they are equally effective at causing circadian disruption, and their use by night shift workers is ill-advised.

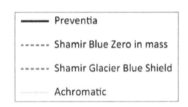

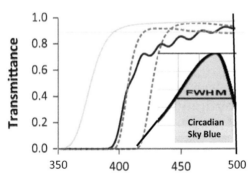

Many of the best-selling "blue-blocker eyewear" brands allow ~90% transmission of circadian sky-blue light and are therefore ineffective at preventing circadian disruption. (Adapted from Carlson (2019) https://doi.org/10.4102/aveh.v78i1.497)

Blue-Blocking Eyewear

Blue-blocking glasses are a rapidly growing $30 million/year market.[221] But most of these products unfortunately block the wrong blue.[222] There are many different color wavelengths in the blue part of the spectrum, as was discussed in Chapter 4: *Human Light Interaction,* and they have quite different biological effects. 420nm violet blue stimulates alertness, 440 indigo blue can damage the eyes but only at very bright outdoor sunlight intensities, 460 nm royal blue can cure jaundice in newborns and 480 nm sky blue is the key daytime synchronizer for circadian clocks, but disrupts our clocks and health at night.

The best-selling blue blocker glasses are blocking blue mostly below 450 nm. But the peak circadian blue effect is at 480 nm which these clear-looking glasses barely touch. The giveaway is when the glasses are only lightly tinted to make them look attractive. In contrast, glasses that remove most circadian active blue wavelengths (between 440-495nm) are distinctly yellow-orange in color.

There are several vendors, including Cyxus, Rhythm Optics, Swannies and UVEX, offering glasses that block 98% or more 400-495 nm blue light. However, they also block more green light than is necessary for light-adapted people and therefore can impair color vision.[223] The challenge our team at the Circadian Light Research Center, University of Toronto, and UC Berkeley addressed was how to balance 440-495 nm circadian wavelength blocking with the best visual performance. The result was BLUESAFE 24, sold by CircadianEye LLC, which are glasses that maximize lens brightness and functional color vision while providing strong circadian protection.[224]

EssilorLuxottica, the world's largest eyewear company, sells lenses with a Crizal Prevencia coating, which blocks 20% of the light from wavelengths between 400-455 nm, creating a slight blue reflective tint.[225] They justify this by claiming that 425-450 nm wavelengths can damage the eye. As discussed in Chapter 4: *Human-Light Interaction*, this is only an issue in very bright sunlight, but never a problem at indoor intensity levels that are 100 - 1000 times less. Blocking only 20% of these blue wavelengths in bright sunlight seems of small value when any reasonably effective sunglasses will block 50-60% of light from all visible wavelengths. For indoor use, where 425-450 nm wavelengths present no hazard, upgrading to a Crizal Prevencia coating at approximately $200 puts money in the pocket of the optician with no benefit to you.

But what about the other claims that blue-blocking glasses reduce eye fatigue, digital eyestrain, or computer vision syndrome – (the technical name is "Asthenopia")? Studies comparing computer users with eyewear that blocked 99% of all blue wavelengths between 400 and 500 nm, and the same people with glasses that let through all the blue light, have shown there is no reduction of objectively measured work-related asthenopia with the blue-blocking lenses.[226]

Effective Blue-Blocking

Blue-blocking glasses can effectively prevent circadian disruption in the evening, provided you purchase the correct eyewear that filters out the 440-495 nm circadian potent wavelengths. Even in well-lit rooms, melatonin levels can be nearly fully restored in the evening and at night.[227] And gene markers of circadian disruption such as Per and BMal are returned to normal. Sleep latency – the time it takes to fall asleep – is shortened especially in people with sleep disorders, including those caused by jet lag and shift work.

A single evening's use of blue-blocking glasses doesn't have much effect on sleep. However, when circadian blue-blocking eyewear is used regularly for the 3 hours before bed for more than a week, sleep quality is increased, and glucose metabolism and insulin resistance are significantly improved.[228]

When blue-blocking eyewear in the evening is used in conjunction with 480nm sky-blue light treatments in the mornings, robust effects on performance are obtained. Teenagers who were previously sleep-deprived and sleepy in the mornings showed more consistent sleep patterns, improved alertness, and better performance on math tests after 3-4 weeks of the combined evening blue blockers and morning blue light treatments.[229] MRI analysis showed improved brain connectivity and growth in the dentate gyrus areas of the brain associated with memory formation and learning.

The better option is usually to change the lighting, as that requires no active management, and has less opportunity for error. But, it is good to know that you can control your own light diet, even if your indoor lighting is far from ideal.

In this chapter, you have learned:

1. You must be proactive in asking for healthy circadian lighting in the spaces where you and your family spend significant time.

2. Understanding the WIIFMs for stakeholders and decision makers and knowing the spec locks for true circadian lighting, are crucial to campaigning to change the lights in places you do not control.

3. Even in places where you cannot change the lights, you can use blue-emitting lamps or eyewear during the day and evidence-based blue-blocking eyewear in the evening.

12

Light Pollution and Biodiversity

We must consider the harm caused to the other 8.7 million species on Earth by our unrestrained use of electric light, and how we can protect biodiversity.

Early in the morning of February 4th, 1993, an orbiting Russian satellite named "Znamya 2" (meaning "Banner") deployed a large mirror to reflect the sun's rays onto the dark side of the Earth.[230] The dream of the engineers was to banish the night and save billions of dollars in electricity. By increasing the length of the day, they sought to boost productivity in farms and cities in the then-Soviet Union. A constellation of synchronized satellites was planned each carrying a 200-meter mirror illuminating a ten-square-mile area on Earth with a brightness nearly 100 times greater than moonlight. Far from their thoughts was the devastating effects this would have on the health of humans and the other 8.7 million species which are evolution-optimized to live under the natural 24-hour light-dark cycle.[231]

Life on Earth dodged that bullet with the collapse of the Soviet Union, but now the profusion of cheap outdoor LED light presents an even more significant threat. As LED prices have plummeted and the cost of powering them has fallen because of escalating lumens per watt efficiency, the appetite to use more lights has increased, blunting the promised energy savings. Professor Lucas Davis at the UC Berkeley Haas School of Business believes we should embrace this, claiming "More and brighter lighting for our homes, businesses and public spaces can make us happier, more productive and safer. ... LEDs are great even if they won't necessarily result in large net energy savings."[232] But this viewpoint overlooks the negative impact of outdoor electric light at night on the Earth's flora and fauna.

Outdoor lighting seems particularly at risk of low price induced increases in LED consumption.(istock.com/welcomia)

By 2005, 1.5% of the world's electricity production was used for outdoor lighting. We were pumping 11 quadrillion lumen hours of light into the nighttime outdoor world (measured in Peta-Lumen-Hours/year, where a Peta is 1015 lumens).[233] Total global electricity production has since increased at a rate of 3%

per year, but the hope that LEDs would reduce electricity use has not borne out. Any efficiency gains in producing lumens have been outstripped by the increased use of brighter outdoor LED lights as prices fell.

To address this challenge to the millions of diverse lifeforms on this planet, we must think differently about indoor versus outdoor lighting.

Our Rights Indoors

We are entitled to control the lighting of our own indoor domain for the benefit of ourselves and our family members, without having to be concerned for other species, besides our pets and house plants. Most of us have no compunction about exterminating rodents or cockroaches and setting traps to catch flies in our own homes. In the same way, the only consideration in selecting lighting inside our homes, schools, hospitals, and workplaces is what will most benefit the health of our family, our colleagues, and ourselves. These lighting specifications are discussed in Chapter 10: *How to be a Smart Consumer* and Chapter 11: *When You Don't Control the Space.*

8.7 Million Other Species Have Rights Outdoors

Outdoors, it is a very different matter. We are part of a highly complex interdependent global ecosystem that we only partly understand. All life forms on Earth evolved to operate most successfully under the natural day-night and seasonal cycles conferred by our rotating planet. Increasing outdoor nighttime light levels above 0.2 lux of bright moonlight disrupts the feeding and breeding behaviors of millions of species, and most of the time, natural light levels are much less at night.

Outdoor lights affect much more than their immediate vicinity. The skyglow from a major city can be seen more than 50 miles away.[234] In densely populated areas of the world, such as the eastern half of the United States and Western Europe, very few areas are not impacted by light pollution at night. The brightness is increased on cloudy nights because electric light reflects off the clouds. By 2016, 88% of Europe and 47% of the United States, had night sky brightness at least 8% above the natural level.[235] And sky brightness continues to increase by 7-10% per year.[236]

Disrupted Food Webs

Nature is comprised of complex sets of food webs with food chains that are critical to the survival of each species. Not every species in a food chain has to be directly disrupted by light at night. All it takes is for some microbes, plants, insects, or animals

Life on Earth depends on complex food webs unique to each habitat. The effects of light at night on any species on the food chain can affect the survival of all other species above it. (iStock.com/blueringmedia)

in the food chain to be affected, and everything else above them in the food chain suffers.

The primary producers in terrestrial food chains are plants that use the sun's energy to photosynthesize inorganic nutrients (e.g., phosphates, nitrates) into organic food (e.g., leaves and flowers) that other species can eat. The primary consumers are the herbivores that eat the plants (e.g., caterpillars or grasshoppers). Secondary consumers are the carnivores that eat the primary consumers (e.g., songbirds or mice). Above them in the food chain are the apex predators such as hawks, which feast on the secondary consumers such as songbirds or mice. The players at each level, of course, depend on the ecosystem and climate.

Electric light at night (abbreviated as LAN) significantly impacts these food chains. Primary producer plants in food chains have been disrupted by LAN, long before the introduction of LED lights. When High Pressure Sodium streetlights were first installed in the 1970s maize crops alongside main roads grew rapidly but failed to flower, and the normal development of soya beans near bright floodlights was disrupted.[237] The responses to LAN are highly varied. Some species of grass grow more rapidly while others are suppressed, changing the nature of the food supply to the detriment of some species and the advantage of others.

Similarly, primary consumer populations are disrupted by LAN, both because of changes in food supply, and because of direct effects on their development. Caterpillar populations under white LED streetlights are reduced by almost 50% in the hedgerows and by 33% in the grass verges of British country roads.[238] This reduces the food supply to secondary consumers such as the British songbirds that nest in those hedgerows. And so the impact of LAN ripples through the entire food chain.

In 1897, soon after the first electric lights were installed along the country streets of England, concerns were already being raised about their impact on songbirds:

> "With the exception of the finches, all the English songbirds may be said to be insectivorous, and their diet consists chiefly of vast numbers of very small insects which they collect from the grass and herbs before the dew is dry. As the electric light is finding its way for street illumination into the country parts of England, these poor winged atoms are slain by thousands at each light every warm summer evening....The fear is expressed, that when England is lighted from one end to the other with electricity the song birds will die out from the failure of their food supply." [239]

Songbirds may not have died out in England, but their populations have shrunken considerably. The population of the most famous of British songbirds immortalized in John Keat's poem "*Ode to a Nightingale*" has declined by 92% since the first blue-rich lights were widely introduced in the 1970s. Over the same time frame, turtle doves have declined 98%, willow tits by 94% and starlings by 82%, to name just a few.[240]

Aquatic Food Chains

In aquatic food chains, the primary photosynthesizing producers include algae, which live near the surface where they can harvest the most sunlight. Their primary consumers are zooplankton, thousands of species of small animals, including shrimp and other crustaceans, which are highly sensitive to light and hide deep in the water during the day and come up

THE LIGHT DOCTOR | 215

to feed on the algae at night. The secondary consumers are the fish that eat the zooplankton.

Electric light falling on any body of water at night forces the zooplankton to stay deeper below the surface, so they are less visible to the fish that prey on them.[241] This behavior starves the fish of their primary food supply, and at the same time, allows the uneaten algae to bloom, contaminating the surface of the water. Fish populations, as a result, plummet.

Sensitivity to Light

Worldwide, around 30% of vertebrates and more than 60% of invertebrates are nocturnal.[242] Nocturnal species are generally much more sensitive to light at night than day-active species. Their eyes are often adapted to detect lower light levels at the expense of visual resolution.

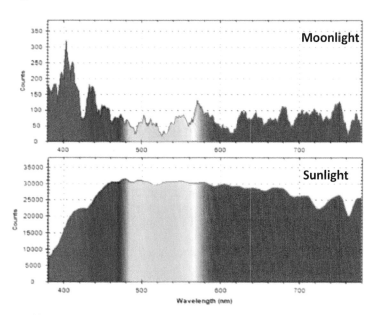

In addition to being up to a million times dimmer, the spectral power distribution of moonlight is distinctly different than that of sunlight.
(Breitler et al. (2020) https://doi.org/10.1186/s12870-020-2238-4*)*

The spectral composition of moonlight is quite different from sunlight.[243] The peak energy is deep in the violet
at around 400 nm, compared to sky blue 480 nm peak
energy in sunlight – although the peak of the daylight
spectrum can vary with weather conditions. It is therefore
not surprising that nocturnal species gauge the brightness
of light from a different range of spectral wavelengths than
humans. Whereas humans experience maximum brightness
at 555 nm in the green, nocturnal species are often more
sensitive to shorter wavelengths sometimes down into the
ultraviolet. Even small changes in lunar brightness from a
new to a full moon can trigger critical reproductive and
developmental effects.

Outdoor lights, besides raising brightness way above
natural moonlight, introduce unnatural spectra into the
nocturnal landscape, whether High Pressure Sodium lights
emitting yellow-orange wavelengths, or conventional LEDs
with a peak at 450 nm royal blue. We have only scratched
the surface of how each of the millions of nocturnal species
with diverse spectral sensitivities are affected. This greatly
impacts biodiversity because electric lighting is fundamentally
changing the photic environment.

Some species are attracted by light, others are repelled
by it, yet others may have their life-critical behaviors and
physiological systems disrupted. Let's look at some examples
of electric light effects.

- **Circadian, Circalunar & Circannual Disruption:** Both
  day-active and nocturnal species rely on the precise timing of natural light day cycles, whether they are the daily
  sunrise and sunset, the approximately monthly waxing
  and waning of the moon, or the changes in day length

and night length with the seasons of the year. Disruption of these natural light-dark cycles impacts the metabolism, immunity, and risk of cancer and other diseases, just like humans. However, the sensitivity to low levels of light is much greater. For example, in nocturnal rodents it takes only 0.03 lux of light (moonlight levels) to suppress melatonin significantly.[244] Furthermore, LAN affects feeding behaviors, and reproductive success to a greater extent than it does in mankind.

- **Spatial Disorientation & Navigation:** Many nocturnal species use the moon or stars to navigate. Electric light sources can obscure their view of the sky, or provide false signals. As a result, they may fail to find feeding grounds, or to mate and reproduce.

- **Attraction:** Some species are attracted to light, and others are repelled by it. About a third of insects approaching outdoor lights die soon after due to collision, overheating, dehydration, or predation".[245] Millions of birds die each year after colliding with buildings, attracted from miles away by the lights.[246]

- **Loss of Dark Adaptation:** As we discussed, nocturnal species are highly sensitive to light, and may take hours to regain complete dark adaptation after coming close to electric lights. This temporarily blinds the creature and interferes with its ability to find nutrients or avoid predators.

- **Bioluminescence:** Fireflies and certain other species use bioluminescence to emit light flashes to attract mates. Outdoor electric light may mask these signals and interfere with reproduction.

Facing the Challenge

The LED revolution has given us plentiful, cheap, bright light and the temptation to light up building facades, landscapes, sports facilities, highways and backyards. The arguments in favor - aesthetics, usability, safety, and security - have to be tempered by the devastating impact of light at night on the flora and fauna of the natural world.

Lighting our indoor day and night environments is a relatively simple challenge compared to illuminating the outdoor world that is shared with millions of other species, each with its own unique spectral sensitivity to light. The human spectral sensitivity is now well known, so indoor circadian lights can be designed with only one species in mind, as discussed in earlier chapters.

In 2023 Travis Longcore at the University of California,

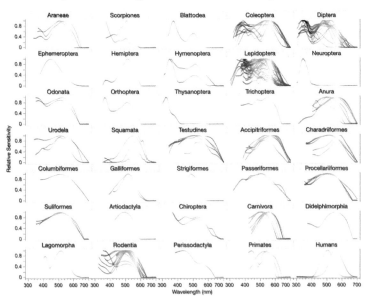

Spectral sensitivity curves by order. Curves are grouped by class (Spiders, Insects, Amphibians, Reptiles, Birds, Mammals), vs human scotopic and photopic curves. (Longcore (2023) https://doi.org/10.1016/j.baae.2023.09.002)

Los Angeles, Institute of the Environment and Sustainability, undertook an exhaustive exercise to document the spectral sensitivity of 320 species of terrestrial wildlife that could be affected by the nighttime lighting of California's highways.[247] These included Spiders, Insects, Amphibians, Reptiles, Birds and Mammals. The lesson learned is that the diversity of responses to light is enormous. There is no ideal one-size-fits-all solution to lighting the natural landscape – other than returning landscapes, wherever possible, back to the lighting conditions of the pre-electric world.

Restore the Night

The environmental light pollution problem with outdoor lighting can be solved with the flick of a switch. Unlike most environmental hazard clean-ups, the solution is instantaneous, has no residual effects, and actually saves money. The contribution from indoor lighting emanating from windows can be addressed by using light-proof curtains, shades, and blinds.

But sometimes we do need to use light outside. It may be for safety and security, avoiding trips and falls by illuminating a pathway or steps or lighting a roadway where pedestrians are crossing the street. But when we do this, we should follow the Five Rules of Outdoor Lighting.

Five Rules of Outdoor Lighting

Rule #1: All Light Should Have a Clear Purpose

Outdoor electric light at night is harmful to many species. Therefore, when we use light outside, it must have a clear purpose. Not all roadway lighting increases safety. It can be just as effective to have reflectors (cat's eyes) marking the edges of each travel lane that reflect light from oncoming headlights, but emit no light themselves.

Rule #2: Light Should Be Directed Only Where Needed

Outdoor lights should be focused and shielded so light is only directed to where needed. For example, streetlights should only illuminate the roadway and sidewalks, and cast no light on hedgerows, grass verges and trees, or into the sky. Pathway lights should not shine into the rest of the garden, or the neighbor's yard, with lighting as low to the ground as possible.

Rule #3: Light Should Be Used Only When Needed

If you cannot turn off the lights completely, consider using motion sensors and automatic timers so the lights are switched on, only when it is necessary. When lights are switched off, even temporarily, it allows birds and insects to escape the fatal attraction of the lights. There is considerable experience in Europe with "dynamic roadway lighting", where lights are dimmed after peak traffic hours with no significant increase in collisions.

Rule #4 Light Sources Should Emit Less Than 2% Blue Content.

While there is considerable inter-species variation, there is less overall disruption to flora and fauna when wavelengths are removed below 500 nm. As we discussed in Chapter 11: *When You Don't Control the Space*, the Hawaiian island of Maui has passed an ordinance that outdoor lighting should have less than 2% 400-500 nm blue. The major LED manufacturer, Lumileds, now produces LEDs that can meet this standard.

Rule #5: Light Should Be No Brighter Than Necessary

Even if you obey the other rules, you should always seek to use the dimmest light levels that will meet your objectives. Many species that co-habit this planet with us are highly sensitive to light levels above starlight, and our well-being depends on a flourishing biodiverse ecosystem.

In this chapter, you have learned:

1. Our unrestrained use of cheap outdoor LED light is increasing the brightness of the night sky by 7-10% per year.

2. We are entitled to control the lighting of our indoor domain for the benefit of ourselves and our family members, but outdoors is a very different matter because light at night disrupts our planet's fragile ecosystems, which support 8.7 million other species.

3. We must adopt policies that restrict when and where outdoor light is used and limit its brightness and spectral content of short wavelengths.

Resources

How to find healthy circadian lighting products for your home and the other spaces where you spend your time, keep in touch with research updates and obtain up to date practical information on healthy lighting.

Information and Practical Advice

- The Light Doctor website https://thelightdoctor.com/

- Substack: https://lightdoctormartinmooreede.substack.com

- Psychology Today: https://www.psychologytoday.com/us/blog/the-light-doctor

- LinkedIn: https://www.linkedin.com/in/martin-moore-ede-80630a12/

Circadian Lighting Products

The Circadian Light Research Center https://circadianlight.org provides links to evidence-based circadian lighting products including light fixtures, light bulbs, display screens and eyewear.

Footnotes
and References

Introduction: Questions to Ask Before Switching on the Lights

1. This $2.5 Trillion estimate of the global installed base of existing lighting, is of course much larger than the ~$150 billion global lighting market of new sales per year. In 2023 the USA had an installed base of 8 billion light fixtures and lamps, approximately 50% of which are LEDs -- projected to grow to 84% LEDs by 2035, replacing incandescent, halogen and fluorescent lights. Source: Fig 4. 1 in US Department of Energy, *Energy Savings Forecast of Solid-State Lighting in General Illumination Applications, December 2019.*

Chapter 1: Edison's Cancer Epidemic

2. To enable accurate comparisons between different populations, an age-standardized breast cancer incidence rate (ASR) is used which normalizes the age distribution of the population **to** minimize the effect of the population age on cancer diagnosis rate. Breast cancer ASR incidence rates are from GLOBOCAN (2020) WHO IARC. Electrification history is from World Bank World Development Indicators, Access to electricity. Archived at https://perma.cc/8HXS-WK3Q

A variety of other factors besides electric light exposure contribute to breast cancer incidence (number of new cases diagnosed per year). For example, highly electrified Arabian countries such as Saudi Arabia have lower baseline breast cancer incidence rates than Western Europe, which might be influenced by genetics, diet etc. (Basudan (2022) Breast Cancer Incidence Patterns in the Saudi Female Population. Medcina 58: 1617). However, while the baseline incidence is lower it has been climbing rapidly from 11.8/100,000 women in 2001 to 28.8/100,000 in 2020 as blue-rich LEDs dominate the market.

3. Cancer Today (2020) WHO IARC. Archived at https://perma.cc/HPL6-XL45?type=image. The first studies conducted in the last century (1965-1998) showed a 36-70% increase in breast cancer incidence in women who work night shifts. See references # 8, 9 & 10. More recent meta-analyses, however, show a 16% increased incidence in pre-menopausal women exposed to light at night (Urbano T. et al. (2021) Int J Health Geogr. 20: 44). But the baseline level of blue light exposure at night from LED lights and screens is far higher today in the general population not working night shifts, substantially raising the baseline risk in both control and test groups, and reducing the percentage incremental effect of night shift light exposure.

4. https://www.cancer.gov/types/breast/risk-fact-sheet#how-has-the-risk-of-being-diagnosed-with-breast-cancer-changed-in-recent-years Archived at https://perma.cc/HJQ8-UA5F The lifetime risk of breast cancer for American women has been steadily

increasing from less than 10% for women born in the 1970s.

5. Tulinius H et al (1999) Breast cancer incidence and familiality in Iceland during 75 years from 1921 to 1995. J Med Genet 36: 103–107. Also Electrification History: Iceland Electricity Production 2015-2019. Halfdanarson G. (1997) Historical Dictionary of Iceland. Scarecrow Press.

6. Botswana data from World Bank Electrification Database from "Tracking SDG-7: The Energy Progress Report" and Globocan 2020 WHO International Agency for Research in Cancer.

7. Kliukiene J. et al (2001) Risk of breast cancer among Norwegian women with visual impairment. British Journal of Cancer 84: 397–399.

8. Hansen J. (2001) Increased breast cancer risk among women who work predominantly at night. Epidemiology 12: 74 –77

9. Davis S. et al. (2001) Night shift work, light at night, and risk of breast cancer. J Natl Cancer Inst 93: 1557–62.

10. Schernhammer ES. et al (2001) Rotating night shifts and risk of breast cancer in women participating in the nurses' health study. J Natl Cancer Inst. 93: 1563–68.

11. Schneider AP. et al (2014) The breast cancer epidemic: 10 factors. The Linacre Quarterly 81: 244–277. In 1970 there were only 68,000 new breast cancer cases per year in the USA, which increased to 232,670 cases per

year by 2014, and even correcting for population increases, this is a 4.26-fold increase in breast cancer incidence. Notably, this article fails to consider the role of blue-rich electric light. And Moore-Ede M. (1993) *The Twenty-Four Hour Society: Understanding Human Limits in a World that Never Stops.* Addison Wesley, Reading MA.

12. Kloog I, et al (2008) Light at night co-distributes with incident breast but not lung cancer in the female population of Israel. Chronobiol Int 25: 65–81

13. Stevens RG. (1987) Electric power use and breast cancer: a hypothesis. Am J Epidemiol 125: 556–61. And Stevens RG (2009) Electric light causes cancer?: Surely you're joking, Mr. Stevens. Mutation Research - Reviews in Mutation Research (MRR) 682: 1-6

14. Blask, D.E. et al (2011) Circadian Regulation of Molecular, Dietary, and Metabolic Signaling Mechanisms of Human Breast Cancer Growth by the Nocturnal Melatonin Signal and the Consequences of its Disruption by light at night. *J. Pineal Res.* 51: 259-269.

15. Moore-Ede M et al (1982) The Clocks That Time Us: Physiology of the Circadian Timing System. Harvard University Press.

16. Straif K. et al (2007) WHO International Agency for Research on Cancer Monograph Working Group. Carcinogenicity of Shift-Work, Painting, and Fire-Fighting. *Lancet Oncol.* 8: 1065-1066. And Full Report: IARC Working Group on the Evaluation of Carcinogenic Risks to Humans. *Painting, Firefighting, and Shiftwork* (IARC Monographs on the Evaluation of Carcinogenic

Risks to Humans, Volume 98); International Agency for Research on Cancer: Lyon, France, 2010; pp 563-764; DOI:publications.iarc.fr/116. Archived at https://perma.cc/N8DR-2UR6

17. Wise J. (2009) Danish night shift workers with breast cancer awarded compensation. BMJ Clinical Research 338: b1152

18. In 2018 there were 7,631,091,040 people in the world of which 49.58% or 3,783,494,940 were female and since 26% were children under 14 years of age with no risk of breast cancer, there were 2,799,786,250 women at risk of breast cancer https://www.worldometers.info/world-population/world-population-by-year/ https://ourworldindata.org/age-structure

19. Heer E. et al (2020) Global burden and trends in pre-menopausal and postmenopausal breast cancer: a population-based study. Lancet Glob Health 8: e1027–37 https://www.thelancet.com/action/showPdf?pii=S2214-109X%2820%2930215-1

20. American Cancer Society Cancer Action Network: The Costs of Cancer 2020 https://www.fightcancer.org/sites/default/files/National%20Documents/Costs-of-Cancer-2020-10222020.pdf Archived at https://perma.cc/KC45-6KP5

21. 10,000 research studies 2008 to 2022 (PubMed search "circadian" + "light") with an average cost of $200,000 per study https://ncses.nsf.gov/indicators/states/indicator/academic-se-articles-per-1-million-in-academic-rd Archived at https://perma.cc/24QS-L4TV

22. Travis RC, et al. (2016) Night shift work and breast cancer incidence: Three prospective studies and meta-analysis of published studies. J Natl Cancer Inst.108: djw169.

23. See critique by Schernhammer ES. (2017) RE: Night Shift Work and Breast Cancer Incidence: Three Prospective Studies and Meta-analysis of Published Studies. J Natl Cancer Inst (2017) 109: https://academic.oup.com/jnci/article/109/4/djx002/3074376 Archived at https://perma.cc/4TQB-SY7Q

24. WHO International Agency for Research on Cancer (2020) Night Shift Work. IARC Monographs on the Identification of Carcinogenic Hazards to Humans. Volume 124. https://publications.iarc.fr/Book-And-Report-Series/Iarc-Monographs-On-The-Identification-Of-Carcinogenic-Hazards-To-Humans/Night-Shift-Work-2020 Archived at https://perma.cc/QG85-4B3E

25. U.S. National Toxicology Program (2021). *NTP Cancer Hazard Assessment Report on Night Shift Work and Light at Night*; U.S Department of Health and Human Services, National Institute of Environmental Health Sciences: Research Triangle Park, NC, USA, 2021; https://ntp.niehs.nih.gov/ntp/results/pubs/cancer_assessment/lanfinal20210400_508.pdf.

26. Kubo T, et al (2006). Prospective cohort study of the risk of prostate cancer among rotating-shift workers: findings from the Japan collaborative cohort study. Am J Epidemiol164: 549–555. Also: Parent (2012) Night work and the risk of cancer among men. Am J Epidemiol 176: 751–9.

27. Kim KY et al (2017). The association between artificial light at night and prostate cancer in Gwangju City and South Jeolla Province of South Korea. Chronobiol Int 34: 203-211

28. Dauchy RT (2015) Daytime Blue Light Enhances the Nighttime Circadian Melatonin Inhibition of Human Prostate Cancer Growth Comparative Medicine, 65: 473-485

Chapter 2: Goodbye Milky Way

29. Kyba, C et al (2023): Citizen scientists report global rapid reductions in the visibility of stars from 2011 to 2022. Science 379: 6629, 265-268

30. Klepeis NE, et al. (2001) The National Human Activity Pattern Survey (NHAPS): a resource for assessing exposure to environmental pollutants. J Expo Anal Environ Epidemiol 11:231-252.

31. Kyba C. et al. (2017) How bright is moonlight? Astronomy & Geophysics 58: 1.31 -1.32.

32. Wright KP, et al. (2013) Entrainment of the Human Circadian Clock to the Natural Light Dark Cycle. Current Biology 23: 1554-1558.

33. Stothard ER, et al. (2017) Circadian Entrainment to the Natural Light-Dark Cycle across Seasons and the Weekend. Current Biology 27: 508-513.

34. Kelly T. (2022) Do YOU sleep with the light on? The number of Brits who still do might surprise you. Ideal Home June 17, 2022. https://www.idealhome.

co.uk/news/sleep-light-number-brits-still-might-surprise-221683. Archived at https://perma.cc/FH5S-T9G5 Also see #8 Kim (2023)

35. Mason IC, et al (2022) Light exposure during sleep impairs cardiometabolic function. PNAS 119: e2113290119 https://doi.org/10.1073/pnas.2113290119

36. Kim M (2023) Light at night in older age is associated with obesity, diabetes, and hypertension *Sleep.* 46: doi: 10.1093/sleep/zsac130

37. Obayashi K (2018) Bedroom Light Exposure at Night and the Incidence of Depressive Symptoms: A Longitudinal Study of the HEIJO-KYO Cohort. American Journal of Epidemiology. 187: 427-434. And Burns AC et al (2023) Day and night light exposure are associated with psychiatric disorders: an objective light study in >85,000 people. *Nature Mental Health.* 1: 853–862 https://doi.org/10.1038/s44220-023-00135-8

38. Sooriyaarachchi P et al (2022) Shiftwork and the Risk of Metabolic Syndrome Among Health Care Workers. J. Occup. and Environ. Med. 64: e397-e402. And: Wu Q-J et al. (2022) Shift work and health outcomes: an umbrella review of systematic reviews and meta-analyses of epidemiological studies. J Clin Sleep Med. 18:653–662.

39. Moore-Ede, M.C., Sulzman, F.M. (1981). Internal temporal order. In: Aschoff, J., (Ed) Handbook of Behavioral Neurobiology, Biological Rhythms, Vol. 4. New York: Plenum Publishing Corporation, pp. 215-241

40. Fuller CA, Sulzman FM and Moore-Ede M. (1978). Thermoregulation is impaired in an environment without circadian time cues. Science 199: 794-796.

41. Fishbein AB et al. (2021) Circadian disruption and human health. J Clin Invest. 131:e148286 https://doi.org/10.1172/JCI148286

42. Beyer SE et al. (2021) Circadian rhythm in critically ill patients: Insights from the eICU Database. Cardiovascular Digital Health Journal 2:118–125. https://www.sciencedirect.com/science/article/pii/S2666693621000219

43. Davidson AJ et al (2006) Chronic jet lag increases mortality in aged mice. Current Biology 16: R914-R916

    Windred DP et al (2024) Sleep regularity is a stronger predictor of mortality risk than sleep duration: A prospective cohort study. SLEEP 47: 1–11 https://doi.org/10.1093/sleep/zsad253

44. Gamble J. (2017) Early starters. Nature 550: S10 -S11. Pushkala K et al (2018) Differential drift in menarcheal age in blind and sighted girls. Gynaecology and Perinatology 2: 333-339.

45. Roenneberg T and Aschoff J (1990) Annual Rhythm of Human Reproduction: Biology, Sociology or Both? J Biol Rhythm 5: 195-216.

46. Wever R (1979) The Circadian System of Man: Results of Experiments under Temporal Isolation. Springer Verlag.

47. Stephan FK & Zucker I. (1972) Circadian Rhythms in Drinking Behavior and Locomotor Activity of Rats Are Eliminated by Hypothalamic Lesions. PNAS 69: 1583-1586.

48. Czeisler CA, Richardson GS, Zimmerman JC, Moore-Ede M, Weitzman, ED. (1981) Entrainment of human circadian rhythms by light-dark cycles: A reassessment. Photochem. Photobiol. 34 : 239-247, 1981

49. Lydic R, Schoene WC, Czeisler CA, and Moore-Ede M. (1980) Suprachiasmatic Region of the Human Hypothalamus: Homolog to the Primate Circadian Pacemaker? Sleep, 2: 355-361.

50. Moore-Ede M, Czeisler CA, Richardson GS.(1983) Circadian timekeeping in health and disease. Part l: Basic properties of circadian pacemakers. NEJM 309: 469-476..

51. Moore-Ede M, Sulzman FM, Fuller CA. (1982) *The Clocks That Time Us: Physiology of the Circadian Timing System.* Cambridge, Mass.: Harvard University Press.

52. Callaway E and Ledford H (2017) Medicine Nobel awarded for work on circadian clocks. *Nature* **550**: 18. https://doi.org/10.1038/nature.2017.22736

53. Hill SM, et al. (2015) Melatonin: an inhibitor of breast cancer. Endocr Rel Cancer 22: R183–R204. https://pubmed.ncbi.nlm.nih.gov/25876649/

54. Van Den Heuvel CJ, et al (1998) Effects of daytime melatonin infusion in young adults. Am. J. Physiol. 275 (Endocrinol. Metab. 38):E19–E26.

Chapter 3: Clockwork Blue

55. Lydic R, Schoene WC, Czeisler CA, and Moore-Ede M. (1980) Suprachiasmatic Region of the Human Hypothalamus: Homolog to the Primate Circadian Pacemaker? Sleep, 2: 355-361. And Czeisler CA, Richardson GS, Zimmerman JC, Moore-Ede M, Weitzman, ED. (1981) Entrainment of human circadian rhythms by light-dark cycles: A reassessment. Photochem. Photobiol. 34 : 239-247

56. Vujovic F (2022) Cellular self-organization: An overdrive in Cambrian diversity? BioEssays 44: 2200033. https://doi.org/10.1002/bies.202200033. Also Smithsonian Institution https://ocean.si.edu/through-time/ancient-seas/ocean-throughout-geologic-time-image-gallery Archived at https://perma.cc/SYF2-4TTP

57. Office of Ocean Exploration and Research, National Oceanic and Atmospheric Administration, U.S. Department of Commerce. https://oceanexplorer.noaa.gov/explorations/04deepscope/background/deeplight/media/diagram3.html Archived at https://perma.cc/9QNH-6Q7E. Also: Denton EJ (1990) Light and vision at depths greater than 200 meters. In: Herring PJ, Campbell AK, Whitfield M, Maddock L. (Eds) *Light and Life in the Sea*. Cambridge Univ Press.

58. Moore-Ede M, (1986) Physiology of the circadian timing system: Predictive versus reactive homeostasis. Thirtieth Annual Bowditch Lecture. Am. J. Physiol. 19: R735-R752.

59. Amaral FDO et al (2019) New insights into the func-

tion of melatonin and its role in metabolic disturbances, Expert Review of Endocrinology & Metabolism, 14: 293-300, DOI: 10.1080/17446651.2019.1631158

60. Hastings JW (2001) Cellular and Molecular Mechanisms of Circadian Regulation in the Unicellular Dinoglagellate *Gonyaulax Polyedra*. In *Circadian Clocks*, Volume 12 of *Handbook of Behavioral Neurobiology*, edited by Takahashi JS Turek FW and Moore RY. Kluwer Academic / Plenum Publishers, New York.

61. Lord Rayleigh – Facts. NobelPrize.org. Nobel Prize Outreach AB 2023. https://www.nobelprize.org/prizes/physics/1904/strutt/facts/ Archived at https://perma.cc/H2PC-QUGV.

62. Rayleigh scattering is inversely proportional to the fourth power of wavelength, so that shorter wavelength violet and blue light will scatter more than the longer wavelengths. Violet light has a shorter wavelength compared to blue light and therefore it's scattered more – so why isn't the sky violet? It's because our eyes are actually more sensitive to detecting blue light, and the sunlight coming into the Earth's atmosphere is richer in blue than violet. From: Royal Observatory in Greenwich https://www.rmg.co.uk/stories/topics/why-sky-blue Archived at https://perma.cc/U4Y6-Z8CD

63. What Is the Blue Hour? Learn About This Magic Time Between Daylight and Darkness https://www.treehugger.com/what-is-the-blue-hour-learn-about-this-magic-time-between-4867746 Archived at https://perma.cc/7CRL-AXWS

64. L'Heure Bleue Eau de Parfum by Guerlain is an Amber Floral fragrance for women. L'Heure Bleue Eau de Parfum was launched in 1912. The nose behind this fragrance is Jacques Guerlain. Top notes are Anise, Neroli, Coriander, Bergamot and Lemon; middle notes are Heliotrope, Carnation, Violet, Cloves, Neroli, Ylang-Ylang, Bulgarian Rose, Jasmine, Orchid and Tuberose; base notes are Iris, Vanilla, Benzoin, Sandalwood, Tonka Bean, Musk and Vetiver. From https://www.fragrantica.com/perfume/Guerlain/L-Heure-Bleue-Eau-de-Parfum-208.html Archived at https://perma.cc/XD9A-7YNR

65. Above the Arctic circle in winter the Blue Hour can be much longer than an hour. See comment about Tromsø, Norway in https://www.lifeinnorway.net/blue-hour-in-trondheim/ Archived at https://perma.cc/V5WB-WL9C

66. Zagury F (2012) The Color of the Sky. Atmospheric and Climate Sciences, 2:510-517.

67. The ozone layer lies between 9 - 18 miles above the Earth's surface. See https://www.epa.gov/ozone-layer-protection/basic-ozone-layer-science. Archived at https://perma.cc/A779-U4B7 Also: Chappuis J. (1882) Etude Spectroscopique de l'Ozone. Comptes Rendus de l'Académie des Sciences. 11: 137-186.

68. Provencio I. et al (2000) A Novel Human Opsin in the Inner Retina. J Neurosci. 20: 600–605. doi: 10.1523/JNEUROSCI.20-02-00600.2000

69. Mure LS (2021) Intrinsically Photosensitive Retinal Ganglion Cells of the Human Retina. Front. Neurol.,

Sec. Neuro-Ophthalmology 12: | https://doi.org/10.3389/fneur.2021.636330

70. Borjigin et al (2012) Circadian Regulation of Pineal Gland Rhythmicity. Mol Cell Endocrinol. 349: 13–19. doi: 10.1016/j.mce.2011.07.009.

71. Bailes HJ and Lucas RJ (2013) Human melanopsin forms a pigment maximally sensitive to blue light (λ_{max} ~479 nm) supporting activation of $G_{q/11}$ and $G_{i/o}$ signalling cascades. Proc R Soc B 280:20122987. http://dx.doi.org/10.1098/rspb.2012.2987.

72. Hull et al (2018) Suppression of Melatonin Secretion in Totally Visually Blind People by Ocular Exposure to White Light: Clinical Characteristics Ophthalmology 125: 1160-1171 https://doi.org/10.1016/j.ophtha.2018.01.036

73. Thoreson WB, Dacey DM. (2019) Diverse Cell Types, Circuits, and Mechanisms for Color Vision in the Vertebrate Retina. Physiol Rev 99: 1527–1573. doi: 10.1152/physrev.00027.2018.

74. James SR et al (1989) Hominid Use of Fire in the Lower and Middle Pleistocene: A Review of the Evidence [and Comments and Replies]. Current Anthropology 30: 1-26 Archived at https://perma.cc/4BYU-HWB2

75. Baker N et al Candles, Roman, 500 BCE https://www.smith.edu/hsc/museum/ancient_inventions/candles2.html Archived at https://perma.cc/K8MK-PRDJ

76. Spectrophotometer measurements of light emitted by wood fire and candles calculating 440-495 nm circa-

dian blue irradiance expressed as a percentage of total visible light (380-780 nm) irradiance.

77. Circadian Light Research Center (2015). Spectrophotometer measurements of all fluorescent lights on display at Light Fair 2015.

78. Lin S-Y and Kim Y-S (2008) A cool light bulb. SPIE. Archived at https://perma.cc/HZ6B-6HN3

79. Fluorescent Tubes: Sylvania 48" T8, Daylight (5000K) 32 watts 2725 lumens = 89 lumens per watt; GE Fluorescent Bulb, T12 (4100K) 14 watts 650 lumens = 46 lumens per watt. Incandescent Bulbs: GE Reveal 100 watt 1260 lumens = 12.6 lumens per watt; Sylvania soft white 150 watt 2640 lumens = 17.6 lumens per watt.

80. Pattison M et al (2022) DOE BTO Solid-State Lighting Program, "2022 DOE SSL R&D Opportunities," https://www.energy.gov/eere/ssl/articles/2022-solid-state-lighting-rd-opportunities

81. For example a 6200K LED with >25% blue irradiance (440-495nm/380-780nm) is reported in Safranek S, et al (2020): Energy impact of human health and wellness lighting recommendations for office and classroom applications. Energy & Buildings 226: 110365. https://www.energy.gov/sites/prod/files/2020/08/f77/ssl-safranek-etal-2020_EnergyBuildings_energy-impact.pdf Archived at https://perma.cc/ZK3C-33MV

82. Alfred Nobel's will. https://www.nobelprize.org/alfred-nobel/alfred-nobels-will/ Archived at https://perma.cc/NA93-CL8X

83. Associated Press (2016) 5 decisions that made the Nobel Prizes look bad. https://www.statnews. com/2016/10/03/nobel-prize-questionable-decisions/ Archived at https://perma.cc/4949-PQQU

84. Carson R. (1962) Silent Spring. Houghton Mifflin. Also: DDT Ban Takes Effect. EPA press release - December 31, 1972 https://www.epa.gov/archive/epa/aboutepa/ddt-ban-takes-effect.html Archived January 20 2024 at https://perma.cc/TS66-ABK9

85. The Nobel Prize in Physics 2014 https://www.nobelprize.org/prizes/physics/2014/summary/ Archived at https://perma.cc/JN34-B6PN

86. The Nobel Prize in Physiology or Medicine 2017 https://www.nobelprize.org/prizes/medicine/2017/advanced-information/ Archived at https://perma.cc/J96K-UVQB

87. The global overall lighting market estimate is $139.7 Billion in 2023, growing with a CAGR of 4.3%. The global LED market estimate is $99.98 Billion in 2023, growing with a CAGR of 17.6%. Thus in 2023 LEDs represents 71.6% of lighting sales. https://www.fortunebusinessinsights.com/industry-reports/lighting-market-101542 Archived at https://perma.cc/2QXZ-XGGT

88. Utilities and other energy efficiency program sponsors offer incentives (e.g., mail-in rebates, buy-downs, and instant rebates) throughout the United States to promote ENERGY STAR certified bulbs and fixtures, decorative light strings, and ceiling and ventilating fans with light kits. Many of these programs specifically target commercial buildings and reach up to $249 in

savings for LED light fixtures. From https://www.energystar.gov/buildings/save_energy_commercial_buildings/ways_save/upgrade_lighting Archived at https://perma.cc/7FL2-Q85Y

89. American Medical Association Report of The Council on Science and Public Health (CSAPH Report 2-A-16) *Human and Environmental Effects of Light Emitting Diode (LED) Community Lighting* https://www.ama-assn.org/sites/ama-assn.org/files/corp/media-browser/public/about-ama/councils/Council%20Reports/council-on-science-public-health/a16-csaph2.pdf. Archived at https://perma.cc/XJ8K-ZASN Also: WHO International Agency for Research on Cancer (2010) IARC Monographs on the Evaluation of Carcinogenic Risks to Humans Working Group on the Evaluation of Carcinogenic Risks to Humans: Shift work. Painting, Firefighting, and Shiftwork 98: 563-764. https://publications.iarc.fr/_publications/media/download/2945/aaa53adf824806c6e0b36ebdcb4ef93973e43227.pdf Archived at https://perma.cc/N8DR-2UR6. Also U.S. National Toxicology Program (2021) NTP Cancer hazard assessment report on night shift work and light at night. National Toxicology Program, U.S. Department of Health and Human Services. https://ntp.niehs.nih.gov/ntp/results/pubs/cancer_assessment/lanfinal20210400_508.pdf

90. Lieber M. CNN (2018) Blue light like that from smartphones linked to some cancers, study finds https://www.cnn.com/2018/04/27/health/artificial-blue-light-prostate-breast-cancer-study Published 4:41 PM EDT,

Fri April 27, 2018 Archived at https://perma.cc/2Z27-PKLX. Also: Wallace A (2020) New study links blue light from smartphone screens to weight gain https://www.deseret.com/u-s-world/2020/1/25/21080445/phone-weight-gain-sweets-study Published Jan 25, 2020, 12:00pm EDT Archived at https://perma.cc/7GS9-JS8C

91. Chaudhary A (2022) Global Smartphone Revenue Hits Record ~$450 Billion in 2021; Apple Captures Highest Ever Share in Q4 2021 https://www.counterpointresearch.com/global-smartphone-revenue-hits-record-450-billion-2021-apple-captures-highest-ever-share-q4-2021/ Published Febriary 25 2022. Archived at https://perma.cc/V9L5-QX35

92. Use Night Shift on your iPhone, iPad, and iPod touch https://support.apple.com/en-us/HT207570 Archived at https://perma.cc/Q2AC-JABX Also: Galaxy Smartphones: About the Blue Light Filter https://www.samsung.com/in/support/mobile-devices/galaxy-smartphones-about-the-blue-light-filter/ Archived at https://perma.cc/ST4T-9YB4 Also: Fitzpatrick A. (2015) Amazon's Tablets Are Getting a Killer New Feature. https://time.com/4132444/amazon-fire-tablet-blue-shade/ Archived at https://perma.cc/VX9N-CB3Y

Chapter 4: Human Light Interaction

93. Einstein A. (1905) Uber einem die Erzeugung und Verwandlung des Lichtes betreffenden heuristischen Gesichtspunkt *Ann. Phys.* **322**, 132–148, Archived at https://perma.cc/62FA-WB3D

94. How many photons enter our eyes per second when looking at the blue sky on a sunny day? Physics Stack Exchange. Archived at https://perma.cc/38UR-XCYT

95. Mathôt S. and Van der Stigchel S. (2015) New Light on the Mind's Eye: The Pupillary Light Response as Active Vision. Current Directions in Psychological Science, 24: 374-378.

96. Sudimac S. et al. (2022) How nature nurtures: Amygdala activity decreases as the result of a one-hour walk in nature. Molecular Psychiatry. https://doi.org/10.1038/s41380-022-01720-6. Also: McGlashan EM, et al (2021) Afraid of the dark: Light acutely suppresses activity in the human amygdala. PLoS ONE 16(6): e0252350. https://doi.org/10.1371/journal.pone.0252350

97. Deutscher G. (2010) Through the Language Glass: How Words Colour Your World. Henry Holt. New York.

98. Winawer J. et al (2007) Russian blues reveal effects of language on color discrimination. PNAS 104: 7780-7785 https://doi.org/10.1073/pnas.0701644104

99. Thoreson WB and Dacey DM (2019) Diverse Cell Types, Circuits, and Mechanisms for Color Vision in the Vertebrate Retina. Physiol Rev. 99: 1527–1573. doi: 10.1152/physrev.00027.2018

100. Jameson KA et al. (2001) Richer color experience in observers with multiple photopigment opsin genes. Psychon Bull Rev 8:244-61. doi: 10.3758/bf03196159.

101. Plutino A. (2023) Aging variations in Ishihara test

plates. Color Research and Application/ https://doi.org/10.1002/col.22877

102. Delahunt PB et al (2004) Long-term renormalization of chromatic mechanisms following cataract surgery. Vis Neurosci. 21: 301–307. doi: 10.1017/S0952523804213025

103. Gerl EJ and Morris MR (2008) The Causes and Consequences of Color Vision. Evo Edu Outreach 1:476–486 DOI 10.1007/s12052-008-0088-x

104. Allen J (2001) Ultraviolet radiation: How it affects life on Earth. https://earthobservatory.nasa.gov/features/UVB. Archived at https://perma.cc/PTR7-C6VC

105. Vitaliano PP and Urback F (1980) The Relative Importance of Risk Factors in Non Melanoma Carcinoma. Arch Dermatol 116: 454-456. Also: Moriarty C (2018) Vitamin D Myths 'D'-bunked. https://www.yalemedicine.org/news/vitamin-d-myths-debunked. Archived at https://perma.cc/N4GU-JFB7. The problem with Vitamin D supplements is that most people have more than adequate levels of Vitamin D so that most trials of Vitamin D supplements do not show a beneficial effect. See: Pilz, S. (2022) Critical Appraisal of Large Vitamin D Randomized Controlled Trials. Nutrients 2022, 14, 303. https://doi.org/10.3390/nu14020303.

106. Wang SQ et al (2011) Lack of UV-A Protection in Daily Moisturizing Creams. Arch Dermatol. 147: 618-620. doi: 10.1001/archdermatol.2010.406

107. Linetsky M et al (2014) UVA Light-excited Kynurenines Oxidize Ascorbate and Modify Lens Proteins through

the Formation of Advanced Glycation End Products: Implications For Human Lens Aging And Cataract Formation J. Biol Chem. 89: 17111-17123

108. University of Utah. (2023) How to Tell If Your Sunglasses Are Really Protecting Your Eyes. https://healthcare.utah.edu/healthfeed/postings/2018/07/sunglasses.protect.php Archived at https://perma.cc/PZ59-HR8B

109. Revell VL, Arendt J, Fogg LF, and Skene DJ (2006) Alerting effects of light are sensitive to very short wavelengths. Neuroscience Letters 399: 96–100.

110. Bache SE et al (2018) Universal decontamination of hospital surfaces in an occupied inpatient room with a continuous 405 nm light source. Journal of Hospital Infection 98: 67-73 https://doi.org/10.1016/j.jhin.2017.07.010

111. Arnault E. et al (2013) Phototoxic Action Spectrum on a Retinal Pigment Epithelium Model of Age-Related Macular Degeneration Exposed to Sunlight Normalized Conditions. PLoS ONE 8(8): e71398. https://doi.org/10.1371/journal.pone.0071398

112. Cruickshanks KJ et al. (2001) Sunlight and the 5-year incidence of early age-related maculopathy: the beaver dam eye study. Arch Ophthalmol 119:246-50.

113. Essilor (2023) Eyezen™+ Lenses Defend Against Digital Eye Strain* and Harmful Blue Light https://www.essilorpro.com/content/dam/essilor-pro/product-resources/eyezen/Eyezen+_Lenses_Overview.pdf Archived at https://perma.cc/N29C-5SB4

114. Bretschneider E. (2018) A Reality Check on Blue Light Exposure. https://www.ies.org/research/fires/a-reality-check-on-blue-light-exposure/ Archived at https://perma.cc/EZ99-5FXB

115. CIE International Commission on Illumination. (2019) Position Statement on the Blue Light Hazard (April 23, 2019) https://cie.co.at/publications/position-statement-blue-light-hazard-april-23-2019 Archived at https://perma.cc/DUY6-ZH33

116. Moore-Ede M, Heitmann A and Guttkuhn R (2020) Circadian Potency Spectrum with Extended Exposure to Polychromatic White LED Light under Workplace Conditions. J Biol Rhythms, 35: 405 –415. https://doi.org/10.1177/0748730420923164

117. Finlayson L et al. (2021) Depth Penetration of Light into Skin as a Function of Wavelength from 200 to 1000 nm. Photochemistry and Photobiology 98: 974-981 https://doi.org/10.1111/php.13550

118. Lewis R. (2018) From Blue Lights to Gene Therapy: The Intriguing History of Crigler-Najjar Syndrome. https://dnascience.plos.org/2018/02/15/from-blue-lights-to-gene-therapy-the-intriguing-history-of-crigler-najjar-syndrome/ Archived at https://perma.cc/UJ3Q-7XSB

119. Maisels MJ and McDonagh AF (2008) Phototherapy for Neonatal Jaundice. N Engl J Med 358: 920-928.

120. Tripadvisor. When I first opened the door, the room was in green light. Cool. https://www.tripadvisor.com/LocationPhotoDirectLink-g187323-d1735276-i297634559-

Hotel_Gat_Point_Charlie-Berlin.html Archived at
https://perma.cc/NBP4-5SNE

121. Martin LF et al (2021) Evaluation of Green Light
      Exposure on Headache Frequency and Quality of
      Life in Migraine Patients: A Preliminary One-way
      Cross-over Clinical Trial. Cephalalgia 41: 135–147. doi:
      10.1177/0333102420956711.

122. Tang Y-L eta al (2022) Green light analgesia in mice is
      mediated by visual activation of eurons in the ven-
      trolateral geniculate nucleus. Sci. Transl. Med. 14,
      eabq6474. Also: Kluger J (2022) Green Light Exposure
      May Help Reduce Pain and Headaches https://time.
      com/6225133/green-light-headaches-pain-relief/. Ar-
      chived at https://perma.cc/E8GB-WDFV

123. National Museum of American History. Low pres-
      sure sodium lamp, type Na-10. https://americanhistory.
      si.edu/collections/search/object/nmah_751238 Archived
      at https://perma.cc/5G5B-LECN

124. Intel What does it take to build a fab https://www.in-
      tel.com/content/dam/www/central-libraries/us/en/doc-
      uments/what-does-it-take-to-build-a-fab.pdf Archived
      January 21 2024 at https://perma.cc/JG8S-NDTR

125. Chromoviso (2023) Evidence-based lighting for the
      health care sector. https://chromaviso.com/en/ Ar-
      chived at https://perma.cc/VW2W-U6NB

126. Revell VL, Arendt J, Fogg LF, and Skene DJ (2006)
      Alerting effects of light are sensitive to very short
      wavelengths. Neuroscience Letters 399: 96–100.

127. Yang K (2021) Hair Growth Promoting Effects of 650 nm Red Light Stimulation on Human Hair Follicles and Study of Its Mechanisms via RNA Sequencing Transcriptome Analysis. Annals of Dermatology 33: 553-561 https://doi.org/10.5021/ad.2021.33.6.553

128. Shinhmar H et al (2020) Optically Improved Mitochondrial Function RedeemsAged Human Visual Decline. Gerontol A Biol Sci Med Sci, 2020, 75: e49–e52 doi: 10.1093/gerona/glaa155

129. Zhang et al. (2018) Application of red light phototherapy in the treatment of radioactive dermatitis in patients with head and neck cancer. World Journal of Surgical Oncology 16:222 https://doi.org/10.1186/s12957-018-1522-3

130. Spera V. et al (2021) Transcranial Photobiomodulation on Brain Electrical Oscillations: A Potential Therapeutic Target in Alzheimer's Disease. Journal of Alzheimer's Disease, 83:1481-1498.

Chapter 5: You Have the Right to Healthy Light

131. Databridge Market Research (2022) Global Circadian Rhythm Lighting Market by Regions 2023 - 2030 https://www.databridgemarketresearch.com/reports/global-circadian-rhythm-lighting-market. The global lighting market size was $118.33 billion in 2019 with a CAGR of 4.3% providing an estimate of $146 Billion for 2024. Fortune Business Insights, https://www.fortune-businessinsights.com/industry-reports/lighting-market-101542 Archived at https://perma.cc/2QXZ-XGGT

132. US Department of Energy (2022) Biden-Harris Administration Proposes Raising Efficiency Standard for Light Bulbs. December 19, 2022 https://www.energy.gov/articles/biden-harris-administration-proposes-raising-efficiency-standard-light-bulbs Archived at https://perma.cc/7ZBA-9NAZ

133. Commission Regulation (EU) 2019/2020 of 1 October 2019 laying down ecodesign requirements for light sources and separate control gears pursuant to Directive 2009/125/EC of the European Parliament and of the Council and repealing Commission Regulations (EC) No 244/2009, (EC) No 245/2009 and (EU) No 1194/2012 https://eur-lex.europa.eu/legal-content/EN/TXT/?uri=uriserv%3AOJ.L_.2019.315.01.0209.01.ENG&toc=OJ%3AL%3A2019%3A315%3ATOC Archived at https://perma.cc/8KWN-QATM

134. UK Department for Business Energy and Industrial Strategy (2023) New ecodesign requirements for lighting products. https://assets.publishing.service.gov.uk/government/uploads/system/uploads/attachment_data/file/1132532/new-ecodesign-requirements-for-lighting-products.pdf Archived at https://perma.cc/3XVC-TSEH

135. Halper M. (2022) Circadian pioneer says we're not ready for circadian lighting. Does he really mean it? https://www.ledsmagazine.com/lighting-health-wellbeing/article/14232844/circadian-pioneer-says-were-not-ready-for-circadian-lighting-does-he-really-mean-it-magazine

136. Moore-Ede M et al (2023) Lights should support circadian rhythms: evidence-based scientific consensus. Front. Photon 4: https://doi.org/10.3389/fphot.2023.1272934

Chapter 6: Bringing the Outside Indoors

137. The global lighting market size was $118.33 billion in 2019 with a CAGR of 4.3% providing an estimate of $146 Billion for 2024. Fortune Business Insights, https://www.fortunebusinessinsights.com/industry-reports/lighting-market-101542 Archived at https://perma.cc/2QXZ-XGGT

138. Wright KP, et al. (2013) Entrainment of the Human Circadian Clock to the Natural Light Dark Cycle. Current Biology 23: 1554-1558.

139. Lockwood, D.J. (2016). Rayleigh and Mie Scattering. In: Luo, M.R. (eds) Encyclopedia of Color Science and Technology. Springer, New York, NY. https://doi.org/10.1007/978-1-4419-8071-7_218

140. Jarbow C and Figueiro M. (2023) More Daylight = More Sleep, Designing Lighting. https://issuu.com/designinglighting/docs/designing_lighting_inaugural_edition/s/10913761 Archived at https://perma.cc/BQW9-JQME

141. Reid KJ, Santostasi G, Baron KG, Wilson J, Kang J, et al. (2014) Timing and Intensity of Light Correlate with Body Weight in Adults. PLOS ONE 9(4): e92251. https://doi.org/10.1371/journal.pone.0092251

142. Le Corbusier (Charles-Édouard Jeanneret-Gris) (1927)

Towards a New Architecture. 2014 Reprint of 1927 Edition. Martino Fine Books.

143. Chepchumba NF. (2014) History of Daylighting Strategies: A Comparative Analysis Across the Periods. Thesis. Department of Architecture & Building Science; University of Nairobi https://www.academia.edu/831104/History_of_Daylighting_A_comparative_analysis_across_the_periods Archived at https://perma.cc/V464-C8B3

144. Almodovar-Melendo JM. (2018) Lighting Features in Historical Buildings: Scientific Analysis of the Church of Saint Louis of the Frenchmen in Sevilla. Sustainability 10: 3352; doi: 10.3390/su10093352. And Hannah R. and Magli G. (2011) The role of the sun in the Pantheon's design and meaning. Numen 58: 486–513. https://arxiv.org/vc/arxiv/papers/0910/0910.0128v1.pdf

145. Willis, C. (1995) Form Follows Finance: Skyscrapers and Skylines in New York and Chicago, Princeton Architectural Press, New York, NY. pp. 24– 30. And Steadman P. et al (2009) Wall area, volume and plan depth in the building stock. Building Research and Information. 37: 455–467.

146. Ibrahim NLN. & Hayman S. (2005) Daylight Design Rules of Thumb. Conference on Sustainable Building South East Asia, 11-13 April 2005, Malaysia https://www.irbnet.de/daten/iconda/CIB_DC23487.pdf

147. Smithsonian Institute. Lighting the Way. https://americanhistory.si.edu/lightproject/commercial/com_m.htm Archived at https://perma.cc/3BNR-8JJL

148. Boubekri M. et al (2020) The Impact of Optimized Daylight and Views on the Sleep Duration and Cognitive Performance of Office Workers. Int. J. Environ. Res. Public Health, 17, 3219; doi: 10.3390/ijerph17093219

149. Keskeys P (2021) Think Architects Don't Matter? Check out the World's Most Hated Floor Plan. Architizer Weekly Newsletter https://architizer.com/blog/inspiration/stories/worlds-most-hated-floor-plan-munger-hall/ Archived at https://perma.cc/T87A-2XXS

150. Beeson H (2023) UCSB "windowless" design Dorm Dies. LEDs Magazine. https://www.ledsmagazine.com/lighting-health-wellbeing/article/14298211/ucsb-windowless-dorm-design-dies.

151. Nightingale F, (1860) *Notes on Nursing: What it is, and what it is not.* New York D. Appleton and Company 1860 [First American Edition] https://digital.library.upenn.edu/women/nightingale/nursing/nursing.html

152. Boubekri M. et al (2014) Impact of Windows and Daylight Exposure on Overall Health and Sleep Quality of Office Workers: A Case-Control Pilot Study. J. Clin. Sleep Med. 10: 603-611.

153. Gbyl K et al (2016) Depressed Patients Hospitalized in Southeast-Facing Rooms Are Discharged Earlier than Patients in Northwest-Facing Rooms. Neuropsychobiology 74:193–201. DOI: 10.1159/000477249 And: Benedetti F. et al (2001) Morning sunlight reduces length of hospitalization in bipolar depression. Journal of Affective Disorders 62: 221–223

154. California Energy Commission (2022) Building Energy Efficiency Standards for Residential and Non-Residential Buildings. https://www.energy.ca.gov/sites/default/files/2022-08/CEC-400-2022-010_CMF.pdf Archived at https://perma.cc/HG97-EVHM

155. National Institutes of Health (2019) Daylighting – European Standard EN 17037. Technical News Bulletin 93. https://orf.od.nih.gov/TechnicalResources/Documents/Technical%20Bulletins/19TB/Daylighting%20%E2%80%93%20European%20Standard%20EN%2017037%20October%202019-Technical%20Bulletin_508.pdf Archived at https://perma.cc/93AC-4UDT. And: Šprah N and Kosir M (2019) Daylight Provision Requirements According to EN17037 as a Restriction for Sustainable Urban Planning of Residential Developments. Sustainability 2020, 12, 315; doi: 10.3390/su12010315

156. Scartezzini J.-L. and Courett G. (2002) Anidolic daylighting systems. Solar Energy 73:123-135 https://doi.org/10.1016/S0038-092X(02)00040-3

157. Roshan M. and Barou S. (2016) Assessing Anidolic Daylighting System for efficient daylight in open plan office in the tropics. Journal of Building Engineering 8: 58-69 https://doi.org/10.1016/j.jobe.2016.07.002

158. Mathôt, S. (2018) Pupillometry: Psychology, Physiology, and Function. Journal of Cognition, 1: 16, pp. 1–23, DOI: https://doi.org/10.5334/joc.18

159. Zauner J, Plischke H, Strasburger H (2022) Spectral dependency of the human pupillary light reflex.

Influences of pre-adaptation and chronotype. PLoS ONE 17(1): e0253030. https://doi.org/10.1371/journal.pone.0253030

160. Sulutvedt U et al. (2021) Brightness perception changes related to pupil size. Vision Research 178: 41-47

Chapter 7: Tuning to the Right Wavelength

161. Czeisler CA, Richardson GS, Zimmerman JC, Moore-Ede M, Weitzman, ED. (1981) Entrainment of human circadian rhythms by light-dark cycles: A reassessment. Photochem. Photobiol. 34 : 239-247

162. National Geographic Education, Y2K Bug. https://education.nationalgeographic.org/resource/Y2K-bug/ Archived at https://perma.cc/8S94-CGZ2

163. Straif K. et al (2007) WHO International Agency for Research on Cancer Monograph Working Group. Carcinogenicity of Shift-Work, Painting, and Fire-Fighting. *Lancet Oncol.* 8: 1065-1066.

164. Baird CS (2013) How long does it take our eyes to fully adapt to darkness? https://www.wtamu.edu/~cbaird/sq/2013/08/09/how-long-does-it-take-our-eyes-to-fully-adapt-to-darkness/ Archived at https://perma.cc/VKN9-B89G

165. Thapan K, Arendt J, and Skene DJ (2001) An action spectrum for melatonin suppression: evidence for a novel non-rod, non-cone photoreceptor system in humans. J Physiol 15:261-267. And: Brainard GC, Hanifin JP, Greeson JM, Byrne B, Glickman G, Gerner E, and Rollag MD (2001) Action Spectrum for Melatonin

Regulation in Humans: Evidence for a Novel Circadian Photoreceptor. J Neuroscience 21:6405–6412.

166. Provencio I, et al (2000) A Novel Human Opsin in the Inner Retina. Journal of Neuroscience 20: 600-605; https://doi.org/10.1523/JNEUROSCI.20-02-00600.2000

167. Bailes HJ and Lucas RJ (2013) Human melanopsin forms a pigment maximally sensitive to blue light (λ_{max} ~479 nm) supporting activation of $G_{q/11}$ and $G_{i/o}$ signalling cascades. Proc R Soc B 280:20122987. http://dx.doi.org/10.1098/rspb.2012.2987.

168. Rahman SA, Marcu S, Shapiro CM, Brown TJ, and Casper RF (2011) Spectral modulation attenuates molecular, endocrine, and neurobehavioral disruption induced by nocturnal light exposure. Am J Physiol Endocrinol Metab 300:E518-527.

169. Moore-Ede M and Heitmann A. (2022) Circadian Potency Spectrum in Light-Adapted Humans. *J Cell Sci Therapy*. 13:361-366

170. Moore-Ede M., Heitmann A and Guttkuhn R. (2020) Circadian Potency Spectrum with Extended Exposure to Polychromatic White LED Light Under Workplace Conditions *J Biol Rhythms 35(4): 405–415 (2020)*.

171. St Hilaire MA et al (2022) The spectral sensitivity of human circadian phase resetting and melatonin suppression to light changes dynamically with light duration. PNAS 119: e2205301119 https://doi.org/10.1073/pnas.2205301119

172. Boubekri M, Cheung IN, Reid KJ, Wang CH and Zee

PC (2014). Impact of windows and daylight exposure on overall health and sleep quality of office workers: A case-control pilot study. *J Clin Sleep Med* 10(6): 603-611. And: Viola AU, James LM, Schlangen LJ and Dijk DJ (2008). Blue-enriched white light in the workplace improves self-reported alertness, performance and sleep quality. Scand J Work Environ Health 34(4): 297–306, AndNajjar RP, Wolf L, Taillard J, Schlangen LJM, Salam A, Cajochen C and Gronfier C (2014). Chronic artificial blue-enriched white light is an effective countermeasure to delayed circadian phase and neurobehavioral decrements. PLOS ONE 9 (7): e102827. And Takasu NN, Hashimoto S, Yamanaka Y, Tanahashi Y,Yamazaki A, Honma S, and Honma K (2006) Repeated exposures to daytime bright light increase nocturnal melatonin rise and maintain circadian phase in young subjects under fixed sleep schedule. Am J Physiol Regul Integr Comp Physiol 291: R1799–R1807. And: Wakamura T and Tokura H (2001) Influence of Bright Light during Daytime on Sleep parameters in Hospitalized Elderly Patients. J Physiol Anthropol 20:345-351

173. Rahman SA, Marcu S, Shapiro CM, Brown TJ, and Casper RF (2011) Spectral modulation attenuates molecular, endocrine, and neurobehavioral disruption induced by nocturnal light exposure. Am J Physiol - Endocrinology and Metabolism 300: (3) E518-E527. And: Münch M, Kobialka S, Steiner R, Oelhafen P, Wirz-Justice A and Cajochen C (2006). Wavelength-dependent effects of evening light exposure on sleep architecture and sleep EEG power density in men. Am J

Physiol Regul Integr Comp Physiol 290: R1421–R1428. And: Kayaba M, Iwayama K, Ogata H, Seya Y, Kiyono K, Satoh M and Tokuyama K (2014). The effect of nocturnal blue light exposure from light-emitting diodes on wakefulness and energy metabolism the following morning. Environ Health Prev Med 19(5): 354-361

Chapter 8: Creating Healthy Light

174. Illuminating Engineering Society. CIE photopic luminous efficiency function https://www.ies.org/definitions/cie-photopic-luminous-efficiency-function/ Archived at https://perma.cc/5PEN-ZZ7B

175. EnergyStar. Energy Efficiency https://www.energystar.gov/about/how_energy_star_protects_environment/energy_efficiency Archived at https://perma.cc/A32Q-RMQF And US Environmental Protection Agency. Reduce the Environmental Impact of Your Energy Use https://www.epa.gov/energy/reduce-environmental-impact-your-energy-use Archived at https://perma.cc/X59Z-3MWQ

176. Moore-Ede, M. (2021). LEDs must spectrally balance illumination, circadian health, productivity, and energy efficiency. LED Magazine. Available at: https://www.ledsmagazine.com/lighting-health-wellbeing/article/14199941/ideal-led-lightingmust-balance-multiple-objectives-magazine

Chapter 9: Lights as Medical Devices

177. FDA Overview of Device Regulation. https://www.fda.gov/medical-devices/device-advice-comprehensive-reg-

ulatory-assistance/overview-device-regulation Archived at https://perma.cc/G9T3-CWLJ

178. European Union Medical Devices Regulation (MDR) https://eur-lex.europa.eu/legal-content/EN/TXT/HTML/?uri=CELEX:32017R0745&from=IT Archived at https://perma.cc/RA7K-U4HJ

179. FDA General Wellness: Policy for Low Risk Devices: Guidance for Industry and Food and Drug Adminstraton Staff. Issued September 27, 2019 https://www.fda.gov/media/90652/download?attachment Archived at https://perma.cc/QFY8-MPY7

180. Moore-Ede M, Heitmann A., and Guttkuhn R. (2020) Circadian potency spectrum with extended exposure to polychromatic white LED light under workplace conditions. J Biol Rhythms 35: 405-415. https://doi.org/10.1177/0748730420923164

181. Schernhammer E S , and Hankinson S E (2009) Urinary melatonin levels and postmenopausal breast cancer risk in the Nurses' Health Study cohort. Cancer Epidemiol Biomarkers Prev 18:74-79. And: Sigurdordotti et al (2015) Urinary Melatonin Levels, Sleep Disruption, and Risk of Prostate Cancer in Elderly Men. European Urology 67: 191-194. And: McMullan et al. (2013) Melatonin Secretion and the Incidence of Type 2 Diabetes JAMA. 2013;309(13):1388-1396. doi: 10.1001/jama.2013.2710. And: Forman et al, (2010) Urinary Melatonin and Risk of Incident Hypertension Among Young Women. J Hypertens. 28(: 446–451. doi: 10.1097/HJH.0b013e3283340c16. And: Pandi-Perumal et al

(2016) Melatonin and Human Cardiovascular Disease. J.Cardiovascular Pharmacology and Therapeutics. 2: 122-132. https://doi.org/10.1177/1074248416660622 And: Nurnberger et al (2000) Melatonin Suppression by Light in Euthymic Bipolar and Unipolar Patients. Arch Gen Psychiatry 57: 572-578.

182. Cheung et al (2016) Morning and Evening Blue-Enriched Light Exposure Alters Metabolic Function in Normal Weight Adults. PLoS ONE 11(5):e0155601. doi: 10.1371/journal.pone.0155601 And: Mason et al (2022) Light exposure during sleep impairs cardiometabolic function. PNAS2022 Vol. 119 No. 12 e2113290119 https://doi.org/10.1073/pnas.2113290119

183. Lerman et al (2012) Fatigue Risk Management in the Workplace. J. Occup Environ Med, 54:231-58. DOI: 10.1097/JOM.0b013e318247a3b0

184. Moore-Ede and Heitmann (2024) Spectrally-engineered blue-free white LEDs reduce circadian disruption and diabetic risk of light at night. Manuscript in preparation.

185. van Eekelen, Heitmann and Moore-Ede (2024) Implementation of Circadian Lighting in a 24/7 Chemical Facility Control Room. Manuscript in preparation.

186. Grant et al. (2022) Impact of Upgraded Lighting on Falls in Care Home Residents. JAMDA 23: 1698-1704. https://doi.org/10.1016/j.jamda.2022.06.013

187. West et al (2019) An exploratory investigation of the effect of naturalistic light on depression, anxiety, and

cognitive outcomes in stroke patients during admission for rehabilitation: A randomized controlled trial. NeuroRehabilitation. 44:341-351, 2019

188. Killgore et al (2020) A randomized, double-blind, placebo-controlled trial of blue wavelength light exposure on sleep and recovery of brain structure, function, and cognition following mild traumatic brain injury. Neurobiology of Disease. 134: 104679. https://doi. org/10.1016/j.nbd.2019.104679

189. Roser (2020) Why is life expectancy in the US lower than in other rich countries? https://ourworldindata. org/us-life-expectancy-low#article-citation Archived at https://perma.cc/9ZFC-RQRB

190. National Center for Health Statistics (2022) Life Expectancy in the US dropped for the second year in a row in 2021. https://www.cdc.gov/nchs/pressroom/ nchs_press_releases/2022/20220831.htm Archived at https://perma.cc/E65M-WN3D

191. Windred et al (2023). Light at night and modeled circadian disruption predict higher risk of mortality: A prospective study in> 88,000 participants. *medRxiv*, 2023-09.

192. Burns AC et al (2023) Day and night light exposure are associated with psychiatric disorders: an objective light study in >85,000 people. *Nature Mental Health*. 1: 853–862 https://doi.org/10.1038/s44220-023-00135-8

193. US Department of Energy (2020) Adoption of Light-Emitting Diodes in Common Lighting Applications.

https://www.energy.gov/eere/ssl/articles/2020-led-adoption-report Archived at https://perma.cc/R5TX-MQLL

Chapter 10: How to be a Smart Consumer of Light

194. Kalmbach, DA et al. (2017) Genetic Basis of Chronotype in Humans: Insights From Three Landmark GWAS, *Sleep* 40: zsw048, https://doi.org/10.1093/sleep/zsw048

195. Phillips Hue website https://www.philips-hue.com/en-us Archived at https://perma.cc/27FU-RMTB.

196. Penguin Random House website: 1,940 search results (99 webpages) for diet and nutrition books. https://www.penguinrandomhouse.com/books/all-nutrition-dietary-needs?page=99. Archived on November 20, 2023 at https://perma.cc/PL7M-BXDU. This has increased by 59 books from 1.881 in my last search on May 17, 2023 (see my post "You have to love these rejection letters!"), indicating that books on diet and nutrition are being published by Penguin Random House at the rate of 115 new books per year.

197. Moore-Ede M and Levert S (1998) *The Complete Idiot's Guide to Getting a Good Night's Sleep.* Alpha Books. Simon & Schuster, New York.

198. US Environmental Protection Agency. How the Energy Independence and Security Act of 2007 Affects Light Bulbs https://www.epa.gov/mercury/how-energy-independence-and-security-act-2007-affects-light-bulbs Atchived on November 20, 2023 at https://perma.cc/R2VL-RGFG

199. Spectrasol Sunflow: https://www.youtube.com/watch?v=YQmVfBkkZz0 Archived on November 20, 2023 https://perma.cc/3MC5-S5XW

200. Osin Loop https://osinlight.com/ And: Bios Skyview https://bioslighting.com/skyview-table-lamp/

201. Moody R. (2023) Screen Time Statistics: Average Screen Time in US vs. the rest of the world. https://www.comparitech.com/tv-streaming/screen-time-statistics/ Archived November 20, 2023 at https://perma.cc/3E6V-HXAG

202. Korrus (2023) Dynamic Circadian Display. Preview the products on display at display week 2023 https://sid.onlinelibrary.wiley.com/doi/pdf/10.1002/msid.1399

Chapter 11: When You Don't Control the Space

203. Saidane HA et al (2022) An Explorative Investigation of the Effect of Naturalistic Light on Agitation-Associated Behavior in Nursing Home Residents With Dementia: A Pilot Study HERD Health Environments Research & Design Journal 16:19375867221211461 DOI: 10.1177/19375867221146154 And: Grant LK et al (2022) Impact of Upgraded Lighting on Falls in Care Home Residents. JAMDA 23: P1698-1704.e2, DOI: https://doi.org/10.1016/j.jamda.2022.06.013

204. Hippocrates (400 BC) Of the Epidemics. Translated by Francis Adams https://classics.mit.edu/Hippocrates/epidemics.1.i.html Archived January 4 2024 at https://perma.cc/W863-CBME

205. https://chromaviso.com/en/research-practical-evidence/clinical-evidence-the-effects-of-circadian-lighting Archived January 4 2024 at https://perma.cc/F9KG-HRAE

206. https://chromaviso.com/en/knowledge-about-light/circadian-lighting-improves-recruitment-and-retention-in-elderly-care?_hsmi=2 Archived January 4, 2024 at https://perma.cc/8ERW-WZEM

207. https://www.circadian.com/challenges#challenge-cost-reduction. Archived January 4, 2024 at https://perma.cc/6GBX-HVK9

208. DiLaura DL et al (2011) *The Lighting Handbook*. 10th Edition, Illuminating Engineering Society.

209. Brown TM et al (2022) Recommendations for daytime, evening, and nighttime indoor light exposure to best support physiology, sleep, and wakefulness in healthy adults. PLoS Biol 20(3): e3001571. https://doi.org/10.1371/journal.pbio.3001571

210. Moore-Ede M, Heitmann A, Guttkuhn R. (2020) Circadian potency spectrum with extended exposure to polychromatic white LED light under workplace conditions. J Biol Rhythms. 35:405-415. And: St Hilaire MA (2022) The spectral sensitivity of human circadian phase resetting and melatonin suppression to light changes dynamically with light duration. PNAS 119 (51) e2205301119 https://doi.org/10.1073/pnas.2205301119

211. CIE International Standard (CIE S 026/E:2018) System for Metrology of Optical Radiation for ipRGC-Influ-

enced Responses to Light. Commission Internationale
de L'Eclairage, Central Bureau Vienna, Austria. https://
cie.co.at/publications/cie-system-metrology-optical-ra-
diation-iprgc-influenced-responses-light-o. Archived
Jan 4 2024 at https://perma.cc/VMW7-Z2QR And:
Circadian Lighting Design WELL v2 Q4 2023 https://
v2.wellcertified.com/en/wellv2/light/feature/3 Archived
Jan 4 2024 https://perma.cc/5ZK3-UKKB

212. Underwriters Laboratories. *Design Guideline for Promoting Circadian Entrainment With Light for Day-Active
People, Design Guideline 24480, Edition 1.* Report # DG
24480. Northbrook, IL: Underwriters Laboratories,
2019.

213. American Medical Association (2016) Action of the
AMA House of Delegates 2016 Annual Meeting:
Council on Science and Public Health Report Recom-
mendations Adopted and Remainder of Report Filed.
CSAPH Report 2-A-16 Human and Environmental
Effects of Light Emitting Diode (LED) Community
Lighting https://policysearch.ama-assn.org/councilre-
ports/downloadreport?uri=/councilreports/a16_csaph2.
pdf Archived January 4, 2024 at https://perma.cc/
MS2D-WXD7

214. https://www.civilbeat.org/2022/10/new-law-will-make-
maui-turn-down-the-outdoor-lights-to-protect-wild-
life/ Archived January 4, 2024 at https://perma.cc/
UF8S-YQGV

215. https://www.ledsmagazine.com/lighting-health-wellbe-
ing/article/14296284/lumileds-aims-to-take-back-the-

night-with-lowblue-led-offerings Archived January 4,
2024, at https://perma.cc/VJJ3-UJ65

216. Outdoor Lighting Bylaw Adopted at the 2023 Annual
Town Meeting of Nantucket (Effective Jan. 1, 2024) Nantucket Lights, https://nantucketlights.org https://drive.
google.com/file/d/1zyfz-bq8dA_xCkBbPGiHReByuiv-
lu7GO/view Archived at https://perma.cc/3UFR-PHGU

217. https://www.songfacts.com/facts/bob-dylan/tangled-
up-in-blue Archived January 4, 2024 at https://perma.
cc/D4Q3-VM56

218. Lindqvist et al. (2014) Avoidance of sun exposure is
a risk factor for all-cause mortality: results from the
Melanoma in Southern Sweden cohort. J Intern Med
276:77–86.

219. https://osinlight.com/pages/how-does-it-work Archived
January 4 2024 at https://perma.cc/N739-7HDB And:
https://skyviewlight.com/blog/harvard-interventional-
clinical-research-skyview/ Archived January 4 2024 at
https://perma.cc/8X2S-MAAL And: Sunflow biody-
namic circadian LED floor lamp https://litawards.com/
winners/winner.php?id=3756&mode=win Archived
January 4 2024 at https://perma.cc/3MPV-ENNQ

220. Lovato N & Lack L (2016) Circadian phase delay using
the newly developed retimer portable light device.
Sleep and Biological Rhythms 14, 157–164 And: Lau
T et al (2018) Evaluation of a portable light device for
phase advancing the circadian rhythm in the home
environment. Sleep and Biological Rhythms https://doi.
org/10.1007/s41105-018-0167-5

221. https://www.digitaljournal.com/pr/news/prime-pr-wire/focusing-on-the-competitive-landscape-and-ma-jor-rivals-this-report-provides-an-analysis-of-the-blue-light-blocking-glasses-market-share-with-a-7-cagr-growth-rate-from-2023-to-2030-#ixzz8HC5qZEJQ Archived January 4 2024 https://perma.cc/HG7T-TK6V

222. Carlson AS. (2019) A comparison of blue-light trans-missions through blue-control lenses. Afr Vision Eye Health. 78: a497. https://doi.org/10.4102/aveh.v78i1.497

223. https://www.cyxus.com/blogs/eye-care/what-blue-light-glasses-are-best Archived January 4 2024 https://perma.cc/38TR-SFAY

224. https://bluesafe24.com/ Archived January 4 2024 https://perma.cc/U7FM-JJMU

225. Footnote at https://www.essilorusa.com/content/dam/essilorulp/essilor.pdf Archived January 4 2024 https://perma.cc/RE2V-D8CK

226. Palavets T and Rosenfked M (2019) Blue-blocking Filters and Digital Eyestrain. Optometry and Vision Science 96: 48-54

227. Rahman S et al (2011) Spectral modulation attenuates molecular, endocrine, and neurobehavioral disruption induced by nocturnal light exposure. Am J Physiol Endocrinol Metab 300: E518–E527.

228. Nagai N. et al (2019) Suppression of Blue Light at Night Ameliorates Metabolic Abnormalities by Controlling Circadian Rhythm. Investigative Ophthalmology & Vi-

sual Science. 60: 3786-3793. doi: https://doi.org/10.1167/iovs.19-27195.

229. Teicher M. et al 2023 Bright light therapy and early morning attention, mathematical performance, electroencephalography and brain connectivity in adolescents with morning sleepiness. PLoS ONE 18(8): e0273269 https://doi.org/10.1371/journal.pone.0273269

Chapter 12: Light Pollution and Biodiversity

230. https://www.smithsonianmag.com/smart-news/how-russian-space-mirror-briefly-lit-night-180957894/ Archived January 4 2024 at https://perma.cc/7ZJQ-J2VV

231. https://education.nationalgeographic.org/resource/biodiversity Archived January 4 2024 at https://perma.cc/4RYG-GLE9

232. Davis L (2023) Rebound Effect": cheap LEDs mean more lights everywhere. But brighter homes, offices and public spaces are worth having. https://energypost.eu/rebound-effect-cheap-leds-mean-more-lights-everywhere-but-brighter-homes-offices-and-public-spaces-are-worth-having/ Archived January 4 2024 at https://perma.cc/4GKA-MT8B

233. https://ec.europa.eu/health/scientific_committees/opinions_layman/artificial-light/en/l-3/2-technologies.htm Archived January 4 2024 at https://perma.cc/5HZP-M5YF

234. https://skyandtelescope.org/get-involved/rate-your-skyglow/ Archived January 5 2024 at https://perma.cc/JAZ3-5MCT

235. Falchi, F. et al. (2016). The new world atlas of artificial night sky brightness. *Science advances*, 2(6), e1600377.

236. Kyba, C., et al (2023): Citizen scientists report global rapid reductions in the visibility of stars from 2011 to 2022. Science, 379, 6629, 265-268. https://doi.org/10.1126/science.abq7781

237. Sinnadurai, S. (1981) High pressure sodium lights affect crops in Ghana. World Crops 33: 120–122. And: Briggs, W.R. (2006) Physiology of plant responses to artificial lighting..Ecological Consequences of Artificial Night Lighting (eds C. Rich & T. Longcore),pp. 389–412. Island Press, Washington, DC, USA

238. Briggs H (2021) Light pollution from street lamps linked to insect loss. https://www.bbc.com/news/science-environment-58333233 Archived January 5 2024 at https://perma.cc/8797-GHDT

239. Electricity and English songbirds. *Los Angeles Times* 14 September 1897

240. Wallaya N. (2021) Britain's songbirds are in decline — here's how travellers can help. https://www.nationalgeographic.com/travel/article/britains-songbirds-in-decline-how-travellers-can-help Archived Jnauary 5 2024 at https://perma.cc/W9Q9-KBGH

241. Moore MV et al (2006) Artificial Light at Night in Freshwater Habitats and Its Potential Ecological Effects. Chapter 15 in Ecological Consequences of Artificial Night Lighting. Eds. Rich C and Longcore T. Island Press, Washington DC.

242. Hölker, F. et al. (2010). Light pollution as a biodiversity threat. *Trends in Ecology & Evolution*, 25, 681–682.

243. Breitler J-C (2020) Full moonlight-induced circadian clock entrainment in Coffea arabica. BMC Plant Biol. 2020; 20: 24. doi: 10.1186/s12870-020-2238-4

244. Grubisic M et al (2019) Light Pollution, Circadian Photoreception, and Melatonin in Vertebrates Sustainability 2019, 11, 6400; doi: 10.3390/su11226400

245. Minnaar, C.; et al (2015). Stacking the odds: Light pollution may shift the balance in an ancient predator-prey arms race. J. Appl. Ecol., 52: 522–531. And: Owens, A.C.S.; Lewis, S.M. (2018) The impact of artificial light at night on nocturnal insects: A review and synthesis. Ecol. Evol. 2018, 8:11337–11358 And: Cited by Zhou, C. et al (2023) Artificial Light at Night (ALAN) Influences Understory Plant Traits through Ecological Processes: A Two-Year Experiment in a Rubber Plantation in China. Ecologies 4: 704–713. https://doi.org/10.3390/ecologies4040046

246. US Fish and Wildlife Service. Threats to Birds: Collisions - Nighttime Lighting https://www.fws.gov/story/threats-birds-collisions-nighttime-lighting Archived January 6 2024 at https://perma.cc/JNL3-F5XC

247. Longcore T (2023) A compendium of photopigment peak sensitivities and visual spectral response curves of terrestrial wildlife to guide design of outdoor nighttime lighting Basic and Applied Ecology 73: 40–50 https://doi.org/10.1016/j.baae.2023.09.002

Printed in Great Britain
by Amazon

43536271R00159